Civil Engineering Heritage
Northern England

Edited by R.W. Rennison, BSc, MA, PhD, FICE

Other books in the Civil Engineering Heritage series:
Southern England. R. A. Otter
Wales and Western England. W. J. Sivewright
Eastern and Central England. E. A. Labrum

Future titles in the series:
Wales and West Central England (second edition). R. Cragg
Scotland
Ireland
London

Northern England
Published for the Institution of Civil Engineers by
Thomas Telford Publishing, Thomas Telford Services Ltd, 1 Heron Quay,
London E14 4JD

First published 1981
Second edition 1996

A CIP record exists for this book

ISBN 07277 2518 1

Typeset in Palatino 10/11.5pt by Katy Carter
Printed in Great Britain by The Lavenham Press Ltd, Suffolk

Preface

In 1971 the Institution of Civil Engineers formed the Panel for Historical Engineering Works, its object being the recording of details of structures of historical interest and significance.

To publicize its work, and to attempt to stimulate an interest in the history of the profession, the first edition of this book, *Civil Engineering Heritage: Northern England*, was published in 1981, edited by Maurice Barbey, the Panel's first Technical Secretary and, later, Vice Chairman. Other volumes followed in 1986 and 1994.

As a result of the successful publication of the later books, it was decided in 1994 that the first volume should be revised. Its revision has been substantial and it is hoped that it now provides a much greater spread and depth of coverage than did the first edition.

As Editor, I would like to acknowledge the assistance given by many people, not least the late Maurice Barbey who, through his first book, laid the foundations both for those which followed and for this revision. The principal contributors to the book, in its first edition, were Panel members Paul Dunkerley, the late Roy Hughes, the late Maurice Barbey and myself; to those contributors should now be added John Carter and Roland Paxton, the Panel's Chairman. From those who are not members of the Panel, contributions have been received from Norman Hoyle, Bryan Armstrong, Malcolm Tucker, Brian Haskins, Alan Angus and Ron Fitzgerald; their help is gratefully acknowledged.

I would like to thank Bryan O'Loughlin, the Panel's Vice-Chairman, for his work on checking the book's text, verifying references and proffering advice. I am grateful, too, for the assistance so freely given by Mike Chrimes, the Institution's Librarian, in seeking out references, locating the many papers requested and for acquiring illustrations not otherwise available. I must also thank Ted Labrum for the preparation of the Subject Index to the book; his offer of help was greatly appreciated. My thanks also go to Mary Murphy, the Institution's Archivist, for her help in abstracting information and to Carol Arrowsmith and Claire Delgal for undertaking much of the typing of the manuscript.

Assistance from many local authorities, companies and public utilities must be gratefully acknowledged; their help has been considerable. Especial thanks are given to John Cuthbert, Managing Director of North East Water, for so readily allowing me to use some of that company's facilities; to Malcolm Halliman for the processing of many of the illustrations used in the book; and to Stafford Linsley, of the University of Newcastle upon Tyne, for so patiently and willingly reading and commenting on much of the text. Lastly, acknowledgement is made to the Ordnance Survey for permitting the reproduction of maps and the use of grid references.

R. W. Rennison

Contents

Front cover: Central river crossings of Newcastle upon Tyne (I. Bambrick)

Title page: Albert Dock Warehouses, Liverpool (Merseyside Maritime Museum)

Introduction

This book, as its title implies, covers the northern counties of England, from the border with Scotland to the southern extremities of South Yorkshire, Greater Manchester and Merseyside; it also includes the Isle of Man. Each chapter relates to a defined geographical area based principally on county boundaries, although County Durham has been combined with Cleveland as the development of these two counties had much in common. An introduction giving an outline of the area's development, a map and a list of the sites described are provided for each chapter.

The material in this volume has been abstracted from more detailed reports which have been prepared by members of the Institution of Civil Engineers' Panel for Historical Engineering Works. These reports have been registered under Historical Engineering Work (HEW) numbers and the report forms are held in the Institution's library. Each item described is correlated in the Subject Index with its HEW number; Ordnance Survey grid references are given in respect of each entry. Where possible, references have been given regarding the sources used and, in addition, a general bibliography has been included.

An attempt has been made to describe the many examples of our civil engineering heritage: the best of many types of structure; works which played a major role in the region's development; those which illustrate innovation; and those which achieve some special aesthetic quality. Although the Panel's general view is that only items which are more than 50 years old should be included, exceptions have been made where appropriate. As a whole, it is hoped that the content of the book will add to the knowledge of the history of civil engineering and will also indicate the scope of activity undertaken by the profession.

The names of many of the engineers involved are well known, but in addition to these men there were many others, often working in a local context; their contribution was no less important. In addition, an attempt has been made to show the role played by the many contractors who undertook

I

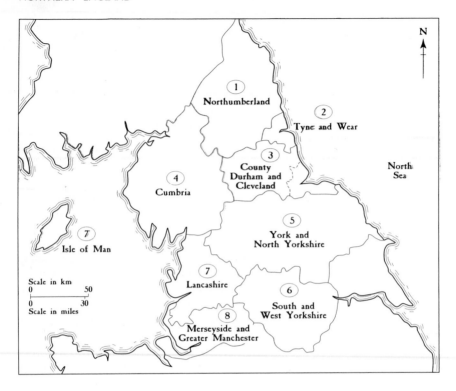

the works described; in the past, their involvement has often been under-stated.

It is hoped that this book will instil in those with an engineering back-ground, and also the more general reader, a better understanding of the contribution made by civil engineers to the economic development of the region and of the country as a whole.

Note on sources
The references listed where appropriate after each subject are ordered ac-cording to their relevance to passages of the text, whether or not they are cited there.

Metric equivalents

Imperial measurements have generally been adopted to give the dimensions of the works described, as this system was used in the design of the great majority of them. Where modern structures have been designed to the metric system, these units have been used in the text.

The following are the metric equivalents of the Imperial units used.

Length	1 inch = 25.4 millimetres 1 foot = 0.3048 metre 1 yard = 0.9144 metre 1 mile = 1.609 kilometres
Area	1 square inch = 645.2 square millimetres 1 square foot = 0.0929 square metre 1 acre = 0.4047 hectare 1 square mile = 259 hectares
Volume	1 gallon = 4.546 litres 1 million gallons = 4546 cubic metres 1 cubic yard = 0.7646 cubic metre
Mass	1 pound = 0.4536 kilogram 1 Imperial ton = 1.016 tonnes
Power	1 horse power (h.p.) = 0.7457 kilowatt
Pressure	1 pound force per square inch = 0.06895 bar

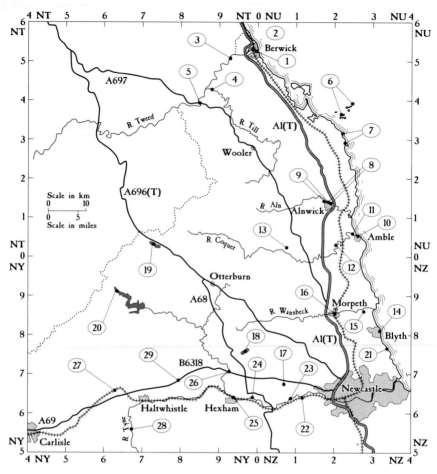

1	Berwick Bridges	11	Warkworth Bridge	22	West Wylam Railway
2	Royal Border Bridge,	12	Acklington Mill Weir		Bridge
	Berwick	13	Cragside, Rothbury	23	Ovingham Bridge
3	Union Bridge, near Berwick	14	Blyth Harbour	24	Corbridge Bridge
4	Twizel Bridge	15	Stakeford Bridge	25	Hexham Bridge
5	Coldstream Bridge	16	Morpeth Bridge	26	Roman Bridges,
6	Farne Islands Lighthouses	17	Whittle Dene Reservoirs		Chollerford
7	Seahouses and Beadnell	18	Hallington Group of	27	Newcastle and Carlisle
	Harbours		Reservoirs		Railway
8	Alnwick Bridges	19	Catcleugh Reservoir	28	Lambley Viaduct
9	Hulne Park Bridges, Alnwick	20	Kielder Viaduct	29	Newcastle–Carlisle Road
10	Warkworth Harbour, Amble	21	Seaton Sluice Harbour		

1. Northumberland

Northumberland takes the form of a triangle, bounded on the east by the North Sea, on the west by the Cheviot Hills and the Pennines, and on the south, except for the southwards projecting Hexhamshire, by the Tyne Gap. Although principally agricultural, there is in the south-east corner of the county—some of it now in the area of Tyne and Wear—an area of coal mining, and it is here that deep and very productive seams were found. To the west, ironstone and coal were exploited in the 19th century at locations such as Bellingham and Ridsdale and, in the 18th and 19th centuries, the extensive working of lead took place in the Allenheads area, in the extreme south-west.

The first improvements in transport came with the building of turnpike roads, with their associated bridges. They were followed by railways, the earliest of the major lines being the Newcastle and Carlisle Railway. The county's most important railway, forming the link between London and Edinburgh, was the Newcastle and Berwick Railway, its best known structure being the Royal Border Bridge over the River Tweed.

The mining of coal in the region led to the establishment and improvement of most of the county's ports, the most significant being the expansion of Blyth which, by 1914, was equal second—with the River Wear—to the Tyne, traditionally the major outlet. In spite of the

Robert Stephenson (1803–59)

INSTITUTION OF CIVIL ENGINEERS

5

the major outlet. In spite of the growth of coal output, the area which now forms Northumberland did not experience an increase in population comparable with that in County Durham. As a result, there were not such high demands upon much-needed services as in the industrial conurbations and in Durham, although the towns of Tyneside came to seek water supplies in Northumberland.

Related to water supply, and one of the interesting developments in the county, was the influence of Sir William George (later Lord) Armstrong and the progressive improvement of his estate at Cragside. There he installed water-generated electric lighting, the first in England, and also perhaps built the first steel bridge. His influence was even wider-reaching in that his engineering works on Tyneside played a major role in civil engineering and supplied hydraulic equipment for bridge and dock installations throughout Britain.

Acklington Mill Weir

6

I. Berwick Bridges

Berwick is the most northerly of England's towns and lies on the north side of the River Tweed, which for some 20 miles forms the border with Scotland. Berwick's vast and unique fortifications date from the late 16th century.

It is not known when the first of Berwick's bridges was built but a ferry was in operation in 1433. The present bridge was constructed betweeen 1611 and 1624. From water level the bridge gives an appearance of both size and strength and has 15 segmental arches, increasing in height towards the Berwick end; the longest span is 75 ft. There are 14 piers, with cut-waters and refuges, making a total length of almost a quarter of a mile.

HEW 694

NT 996 527

In 1928 a four-arch reinforced concrete bridge, the Royal Tweed Bridge, supplemented the old masonry bridge and it now takes the major part of the traffic entering the town. Here, too, there is a gradient rising towards the town so that the four-rib segmental arches increase in span from 167 to 361 ft, the last, when built, being the largest reinforced concrete arch in Britain. The bridge was designed by L.G. Mouchel and Partners and built by Holloway Bros Ltd.

HEW 695

NT 995 528

Also to be seen in Berwick is the pier, some 700 yards long, to the north of the river's entrance; designed by John Rennie, it was constructed between 1810 and 1821.

Sources

HAMLEY W. Berwick's fifty-year-old Royal Tweed Bridge. *Concrete*, Jan. 1979, 20–21.

Ferro-Concrete, Royal Tweed Bridge. Souvenir Number, St Brides Press, London, 1928.

2. Royal Border Bridge, Berwick

The Royal Border Bridge over the River Tweed at Berwick formed the last link in the east coast route of railway from London to Edinburgh. The Newcastle and Berwick Railway (N&BR) had been formed in 1845 and, with Robert Stephenson as its engineer, construction began almost immediately. The viaduct is built on a curve and consists of 28 arches, each of 61 ft span; the rails are 120 ft above the river. The structure has a total length of 2160 ft

HEW 20

NT 993 533

R.W. RENNISON

Royal Border
Bridge, Berwick

and the arches comprise two sets of 14 each, with a stop
pier between them; they have brick soffits but the remainder of the structure is of masonry.

As with the High Level Bridge in Newcastle, Stephenson was assisted by Thomas Elliot Harrison, later to
become engineer to the North Eastern Railway when it
was formed in 1854. The resident engineer was (Sir)
George B. Bruce and the contractors were James McKay
and J. Blackstock. The bridge was opened by Queen
Victoria on 29 August 1850.

HEW 2024

**NT 993 533 to
NZ 248 639**

Also on the line of the N&BR are four other viaducts,
all in themselves substantial structures. They are:
Alnmouth (NU 230 121), with 18 spans of 30 ft and a
height of 70 ft; Coquet (NU 222 038), with nine spans of
50 ft and one of 12 ft, 82 ft high, and built by Richard
Hattersley—his address given as Woodhead Tunnel—
and John Willans Nowell of Ramsgate; Bothal (NZ 215
865), with nine spans of 50 ft and one of 12 ft, 123 ft high,
also built by Hattersley and Nowell; and Plessey (NZ 226
790) with five spans of 55 ft, 90 ft high and built by John
Rush and Benjamin Lawton of York. All viaducts have
masonry piers and arch spandrels, but the segmental arch
soffits are of brick; all are 30 ft wide.

The N&BR was opened between Tweedmouth and Chathill and between Morpeth and Newcastle in March 1847, and between Chathill and Morpeth in July of the same year, although the viaducts were not then complete. The short branch to Alnwick was opened in 1850.

Sources

BRUCE G.B. Description of the Royal Border Bridge over the River Tweed on the York, Newcastle and Berwick Railway. *Min. Proc. Instn Civ. Engrs*, 1851, **10**, 219–244.

Newcastle Courant, 30 Aug. 1850.

Information held by Railtrack plc, York.

3. Union Bridge, near Berwick

Although suspension bridges had been constructed ear- **HEW 143**
lier in America, it was in 1817 that Captain (later Sir)
Samuel Brown, RN obtained a patent for wrought iron **NT 934 511**
cable chain links, at the same time constructing a model
suspension bridge at his works. Although begun after
Thomas Telford's Menai Bridge, which had a much
greater span, the Union Bridge was completed first. For

Union Bridge

five years it was the largest span wrought iron suspension bridge in the world and it is the oldest surviving British example still carrying vehicular traffic.

Advice on the design of the abutments and the tower was given by John Rennie and the bridge is unusual, if not unique, in that it has only one pylon supporting the cables. This pylon, 60 ft in height and of masonry, stands on the north side of the river while, on the south side, the cables are carried over the top of a breast wall and are anchored into rock some 12 ft below the top by means of a cast iron anchor plate.

The bridge has a suspended span of 361 ft and is carried by three pairs of wrought iron chains on each side; they are of Welsh manufacture with eyebar links 15 ft long and carry a road deck 18 ft wide. With its toll-house—now demolished but with its façade incorporated into the anchorage wall—it was opened in July 1820, having been erected in the short time of 12 months. At the time, its cost of some £7700 compared with the sum of at least £20 000 needed for a masonry bridge.

The bridge is now under the jurisdiction of the Tweed Bridges Trust. In 1903 it was strengthened by the addition of steel cables to support the deck in the event of chain failure.

Sources

Kemp E.L. Samuel Brown: Britain's pioneer bridge builder. *History of Technology, Second Annual Volume*, 1977, 1–37.

Arthur B. Reinstatement: Union Chain Bridge. *Consulting Engineer*, Feb. 1976, **40**, 17–28.

Paxton R. and Ruddock E. *A heritage of bridges between Edinburgh, Kelso and Berwick*. Institution of Civil Engineers (EESA), Edinburgh, 1981.

4. Twizel Bridge

HEW 90

NT 885 434

Between Berwick and Cornhill, the River Till is crossed by a medieval stone bridge at Twizel. This elegant bridge has a span of 90 ft, at the time of its construction the greatest of any such bridge in England. The arch incorporates five narrow chamfered ribs; its rise is 40 ft. It is recorded that the bridge was used by troops on the way to the fighting at Flodden in 1513 but its date of construction is not known with certainty; it could be as early as

Twizel Bridge

R.W. RENNISON

1500. The parapets were repaired and possibly rebuilt during the 19th century to increase the width of the roadway, now 15 ft.

Source

JERVOISE E. *The ancient bridges of the North of England.* EP Publishing, Wakefield, 1973, 5.

5. Coldstream Bridge

This bridge, designed by John Smeaton, was built between 1762 and 1767. It was the first of his designs to be built and it spans the River Tweed, at this point the border between England and Scotland. The masonry bridge comprises five main segmental arches, all approximating to 60 ft span, but all of the same radius so that the temporary centring could be re-used. The bridge's piers are protected by 'starlings', formerly of rubble stone but now of concrete, provided to reduce scour damage. Downstream of the bridge a dam was built in 1785 to reduce the problem further.

The spandrels appear to incorporate perforations, but they are purely an ornamental feature and are used also at Perth, Banff and Hexham. The spandrel walls were originally filled with gravel and earth, but by 1828 they

HEW 158

NT 849 401

11

Coldstream
Bridge

had deteriorated. On (Sir) John Rennie's advice, a complete reconstruction was undertaken, incorporating longitudinal walls and voids, work which served until 1960 when the arches were strengthened internally with reinforced concrete. Originally 22 ft in width, the bridge was widened at the same time by the addition of reinforced concrete cantilevered footways.

Smeaton seemingly became aware of the problems resulting from loosely filled spandrels. After 1768 bridges often incorporated hollow spandrels with longitudinal masonry walls; further advantages were that ground pressures were reduced and inspection facilitated.

Sources

RUDDOCK E.C. *Arch bridges and their builders, 1735–1835.* Cambridge University Press, 1979, 80–104.

PAXTON R. and RUDDOCK E. *A heritage of bridges between Edinburgh, Kelso and Berwick.* Institution of Civil Engineers (EESA), Edinburgh, 1981.

SMEATON J. *Reports of the late John Smeaton, FRS.* Longman, London, 1812, **3**, 235–251.

6. Farne Islands Lighthouses

The Farne Islands lie between 1½ and 5¼ miles off the coast of Northumberland and vary in number, depending upon the state of the tide, from 28 to 15. The two main

islands are Inner Farne and Staple, the home of large
breeding colonies of sea birds.

The Longstone Lighthouse is located at the north-east   **HEW 699**
tip of the Farnes and is distinctive as a 66 ft 6 in. high red
and white tower with its light 85 ft above high water. It   **NU 246 390**
was completed in 1826, having been designed by Joseph
Nelson. Following damage in the 1939–45 war it was
repaired in 1952.

The lighthouse on Farne is historically of some interest   **HEW 698**
in that in 1669 Sir John Clayton built a tower there as a
speculative venture, although it was never used. Trinity   **NU 218 359**
House obtained a patent in 1776 and it is thought that the
present lantern murette, which is unique, dates from that
time. The 28 ft 3 in. tower, its light 82 ft above high water,
was constructed, or reconstructed, by Daniel Alexander
in 1811.

The history of Longstone is almost inseparable from
the story of Grace Darling who, with her father, was
responsible for rescuing survivors from the paddle-
steamer *Forfarshire*, wrecked in 1838. The Grace Darling
Museum in Bamburgh is open to visitors from June to
September. Visits to the Farnes may be made by boat
from Seahouses.

Sources

HAGUE D. and CHRISTIE C. *Lighthouses*. Gomer Press, Llandysul, 1975,
81–82.

Trinity House correspondence in possession of the Institution of Civil
Engineers.

7. Seahouses and Beadnell Harbours

Although most of the ports in the North East were developed as a result of the coal trade, others—Seahouses and
Beadnell among them—remained as traditional trading
and fishing ports. Both of these ports were involved in
the production and export of lime with both coal and
limestone available nearby; lime kilns survive at both
harbours.

Seahouses Harbour was developed under the aegis of   **HEW 1988**
the Lord Crewe Estates and the inner harbour, of ma-
sonry construction, was built circa 1786 by Robert Cra-   **NU 224 322**
mond of North Sunderland. Lime exports increased from

that time but eventually ceased in about 1850 with the completion of the York, Newcastle and Berwick Railway. An expansion of the fishing trade led to the harbour's extension in 1899, this work being under the direction of Sir John Coode in association with J. Watt Sandeman. The construction of a 950 ft long rubble-faced north pier then took place together with an east breakwater of a similar length formed in mass concrete; as a result of these works the water surface of the harbour was increased to some five acres.

HEW 1989

NU 236 286

The harbour at Beadnell is smaller, with a water surface of less than half an acre. The jetties forming the sheltered haven were probably built by Robert Cramond during the late 18th century and, following a change in the port's function from lime production to fishing, the harbour walls were raised in 1886, again as a result of advice from Sandeman.

Source

GRUNDY J. et al. (Pevsner's) *The buildings of England: Northumberland.* Penguin, Harmondsworth, 1992, 160–161, 560.

8. Alnwick Bridges

The old town of Alnwick lies to the south of the castle, home of the Dukes of Northumberland. From the north, the castle dominates the River Aln and what was the Great North Road crosses the river immediately to the west of the castle by means of the Lion Bridge, while a mile downstream is located the smaller Denwick Bridge. Both were probably the result of the Duke's munificence.

HEW 709

NU 186 138

The Lion Bridge, so-called because of the 'Percy Lion' on its central pedestal, was built to replace an earlier structure destroyed by flood in 1772, following repairs made after a flood two years earlier. The bridge has been attributed to John Adam but it was more probably designed by his brothers, Robert and James. Completed in 1773, it comprises three segmental spans of 40, 50 and 40 ft respectively, giving the bridge a total length of 159 ft. A land arch at its south end was inserted circa 1825.

HEW 1185

NU 198 138

Denwick Bridge was built by the Duke of Northumberland in 1766, its design attributed to Robert Mylne. The western face of the 56 ft span bridge is balustraded and

R.W. RENNISON

decorated, while the eastern has a solid parapet. It was widened from 9 to 20 ft by means of a concrete arch in 1924, but it is not known whether a balustraded parapet was then destroyed, or whether the structure was decorated only on the face visible from the castle grounds. This bridge is also of finely dressed local sandstone.

Lion Bridge, Alnwick

Source

ARCHER D. *Land of the singing waters.* Speddan Press, Stocksfield, 1992, 156.

KING D. *The Complete Works of Robert and James Adam.* Butterworth, Oxford, 1991.

9. Hulne Park Bridges, Alnwick

Hulne Priory was one of the earliest Carmelite foundations in England and its ruins stand in extensive parklands, the property of the Duke of Northumberland. Apart from its other attractions, the Park contains two iron bridges, both of some interest.

The Metal Bridge carries a carriage road over the River Aln and consists of three arches of 21, 24 and 21 ft respectively, reaching a height of 15 ft. It is flanked by masonry abutments and provides a roadway approximately 11 ft wide. The deck is carried on fish-bellied beams bolted to

HEW 1328

NU 163 153

the edge girders with a cast iron plated deck, now concreted, and a cast balustrade. The design was possibly by David Stephenson, a Newcastle architect, and the ironwork was produced by I. & T. Cookson of Newcastle. Its ornamentation incorporates both the lion and crescent insignia of the Percy family, together with the date, 1812.

HEW 1329

NU 176 150

Also in the Park, and a mile to the east, is the Duchess Bridge, a lenticular footbridge with a span of 74 ft, providing a width of 4 ft. The upper chords are of cast iron while the lower, horizontal, members comprise 1½ in. wrought iron tension bars. It was built in about 1868 and may have been fabricated by the Alnwick Foundry and Engineering Company, which supplied drawings for an earlier proposal there.

Metal Bridge,
Hulne Park,
Alnwick

10. Warkworth Harbour, Amble

The port of Amble is the smallest of the coal-exporting ports which served the Northumberland and Durham coalfield. The River Coquet and the port were, for many years, under the jurisdiction of the Duke of Northumberland, but in 1837 the Warkworth Harbour Commission was formed to improve the port. Reports on its condition were sought from several engineers—Robert Nicholson, John Murray and James Leslie—but it was (Sir) John Rennie who, in 1838, provided plans for the construction of breakwaters at the river's entrance.

HEW 1990

NU 27 05

His recommendations were put in hand, the principal item being the forming of a breakwater to the north of the river's mouth. It took the form of a masonry structure some 2300 ft long, with sloping faces. A smaller south breakwater was also provided. The main contractors, who sublet the actual construction work, were Kingscote and Brown and, not without problems, work was completed by 1849; the north breakwater had cost some £100 000 and the south approximately £16 000.

To improve the port further the commissioners considered building docks but, although proposals were made in 1844 and 1850, no work resulted. By 1854, however, a branch railway had been brought to the port by the North Eastern Railway and staiths had been built so that coal could be shipped.

Messrs Meik and Nesbitt were appointed as consulting engineers in 1869 and, as a result of their recommendations, extensive dredging of the harbour was undertaken; in 1870 the rate of this work was in the order of 250 000 tons per annum. A relatively small tidal basin was formed but the port, serving only a small and discrete coalfield, did not prosper as did other ports in the region.

In the early years of the 20th century the north pier was extended but problems—deterioration and undermining by wave action—continued to be encountered and ironworks slag was brought from Hartlepool and Middlesbrough for its repair. Annual coal shipments rose to more than 500 000 tons by 1914, modest in relation to other nearby ports, but the demise of mining in the region led to demolition of the staiths and the dismantling of the railway.

Source

RENNISON R.W. *The development of the North East Coal Ports, 1815–1914.* University of Newcastle upon Tyne, PhD thesis, 1987.

11. Warkworth Bridge

HEW 696

NU 249 062

The bridge at Warkworth is the lowest crossing of the River Coquet and consists of two segmental arches, each having four wide ribs, the outer ones chamfered, as are also its double arch rings. The central pier has massive cutwaters. Founded on rock to the north, the bridge's central pier and south abutment are based on timber platforms, protected by sheet piles and a stone apron. The width between parapets is 11 ft.

The bridge is thought to have been built at the end of the 14th century and it includes a defensive tower at its southern end. The similar, but better-known, Monnow bridge at Monmouth has the tower actually on the bridge structure.

12. Acklington Mill Weir

HEW 396

NU 202 029

On the River Coquet stands a masonry weir or dam, unusual in that its downstream face is vertical. The dam, one of several on the river, was built in 1776 by John Smeaton to provide water power for a nearby ironworks. Curved in plan, to a radius of 170 ft, the dam is supported by masonry abutments on the river banks, 142 ft apart.

The rubble core is faced with dressed masonry and the structure is 8 ft high with a base of the same width. A feature of the dam, and specified by Smeaton, was that during construction the river was diverted through the abutments in conduits 2 ft square, incorporated for the purpose.

Sources

SMEATON J. *Reports of the late John Smeaton, FRS.* Longman, London, 1812, **2,** 324.

SMEATON J. *Designs,* 1741–92, **2,** 56–58.

13. Cragside, Rothbury

The Cragside estate was purchased in 1863 by Sir William George (from 1887, Baron) Armstrong. A modest house was built by him but the name of its architect is not known. From 1869 the house was successively improved and enlarged under the direction of Richard Norman Shaw and it was noted later by *The Times* that it was 'among the most remarkable of his houses'.

In 1838 Armstrong, a solicitor, had begun the development of the use of hydraulic power and among his first works at Cragside was the construction in 1866 of Tum-

R.W. RENNISON

Iron Bridge, Cragside

HEW 1991

NU 070 025

bleton Reservoir. The reservoir's earth embankment is 35 ft in height and its purpose was to supply water to power a hydraulic engine which, in turn, supplied spring water to the house. Although not recorded, it is possible that the reservoir was designed by John Frederic Bateman, at that time associated with the Newcastle and Gateshead Water Company, which Armstrong had been instrumental in founding and of which he had been chairman until 1864. A feature of the reservoir is the unusual form of its overflow, incorporated into the valve tower.

Later, two further reservoirs were built at Nellie's Moss between 1870 and 1885, between them holding approximately 35 million gallons. They were used to power a generator supplying the house with electricity, first by arc lamps and then in 1880, by incandescent lamps installed by Joseph Wilson Swan. Cragside is reputedly the first house lit by a water-powered incandescent system.

HEW 1052

NU 072 022

In Cragside grounds, and providing a footway over the Debdon Burn, is the Iron Bridge, almost certainly of steel and, as such, one of the earliest examples of that material's use; it was built between 1870 and 1875. This most elegant and graceful bridge has a main span of 64 ft and its level footway is at a height of 35 ft. Built in Newcastle at Armstrong's Elswick Works it was, according to Richards, designed by Shaw in 1864.

The house and grounds are now in the ownership of the National Trust.

Sources

The Times, 19 Nov. 1912.

Cragside, Northumberland. National Trust, 1983.

RICHARDS J.M. *The National Trust book of bridges*. Jonathan Cape, London, 70.

14. Blyth Harbour

HEW 1992

NZ 32 81

Coal was first shipped from Blyth circa 1600 and, to protect the harbour, the North Dyke, a rough mound of stones, was formed in 1756. To guide vessels into the river, leading lights were provided in 1788; of these only the High Light (NZ 320 814) remains.

At the instigation of Sir Matthew White Ridley, effec-

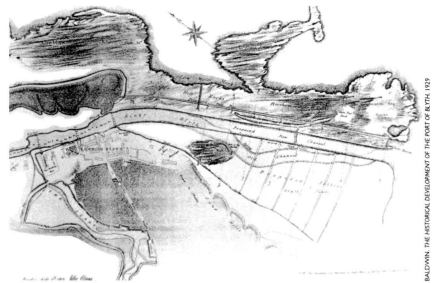

BALDWIN, THE HISTORICAL DEVELOPMENT OF THE PORT OF BLYTH, 1929

Blyth Harbour
Proposals,
Rennie, 1814

tive owner of the port, John Rennie recommended in 1814 that a north breakwater be formed further to protect the river's mouth while, on the south bank, jetties should be built to allow the bank to silt up and so permit land reclamation to be effected; these jetties would also reduce the width of the river and so increase its velocity and, in turn, increase natural scouring.

It was not until 1854 that the Blyth Harbour and Dock Company was formed and under James Abernethy work began on the construction of a breakwater, its line similar to Rennie's proposal. In 1862, Thomas Meik was appointed as engineer and, under him, further improvements were undertaken, not least the dredging of the harbour and the construction of training walls.

Due to some shortcomings on the part of the Company, the Blyth Harbour Commission was formed in 1882 and J. Watt Sandeman was appointed as engineer. Under his supervision both the north and south piers were rebuilt and the rate of dredging was increased. The pier, originally of timber construction, was protected by concrete. The greatest improvements, however, came as a result of co-operation with the North Eastern Railway. In 1896 the North Shore coal staiths (NZ 314 823), a timber structure some 2400 ft long, were built jointly, the Com-

21

missioners providing the river works and the North Eastern Railway the superstructure. Later, the North Breakwater was extended to a length of 4600 ft and a new lighthouse built in 1907; by this date the harbour extended to some 40 acres, all tidal water.

The last of the major works, another joint venture, was the building of the West Staiths (NZ 306 830), completed in 1925 and still in operation in 1995; they allowed two ships to load simultaneously and provided a water depth of 30 ft. By 1914 coal shipments totalled 5 million tons per annum.

In 1993, nine wind turbines were erected by Border Wind Ltd on the East Pier; each turbine can generate 300 kW, so providing a total capacity of 2.7 MW.

Sources

Scott M. Description of a breakwater at the Port of Blyth; and of improvements in breakwaters, applicable to harbours of refuge. *Min. Proc. Instn Civ. Engrs*, 1858–59, **18**, 72–161.

Baldwin C.E. *The historical development of the Port of Blyth*, Blyth Harbour Commission, Newcastle upon Tyne, 1929.

15. Stakeford Bridge

HEW 1385

NZ 272 860

Until 1910 the River Wansbeck at Stakeford was crossed only by a ford, but in that year a reinforced concrete bridge was built by public subscription. Designed by L.G. Mouchel and Partners, the bridge comprises six spans, each of 44 ft, supported on 48 in. diameter reinforced concrete piers. Both abutments and piers are founded on 14 in. by 14 in. concrete piles up to 27 ft long. The piers are arranged in pairs, on a skew of 20°, and are diagonally and horizontally braced.

Originally 24 ft wide, the bridge was widened to 30 ft in 1937 by means of an extension on the downstream side. The designer for this later work was D. Balfour and Son and the contractors were Brims & Co. The bridge was strengthened in 1969 using in situ reinforced concrete beams.

Source

Mouchel L.G. *Mouchel–Hennebique ferro-concrete*. Mouchel, London, 1921, 340.

TELFORD DESIGNS, 1839

Morpeth Bridge.

16. Morpeth Bridge

In the town of Morpeth, forming part of the former Great North Road, a bridge designed by Thomas Telford crosses the River Wansbeck. Its costs were met by public subscription and it replaced an earlier structure, the remains of which now support a footbridge.

The bridge has three spans of 40, 50 and 40 ft respectively and is unusual in the form of its arches, so-called *cornes-de-vache*, which form funnelled entries to the spans. In 1774 Perronet had built a five-span bridge of similar form to cross the River Seine at Neuilly and Telford had used the same type of arch for his Over Bridge at Gloucester; completed in 1828, it comprised a single span of 150 ft.[1] It is possible that a similar arch was at first considered for Morpeth but it was recorded by Rickman that it was considered 'impossible to introduce an edifice of such magnificence; utility was therefore all that could be attempted'.[2]

Telford first intended that the bridge's abutments and piers be founded on traditional bases but as work progressed it was found necessary to use bearing piles to pass through the poorer materials and secure a firm base on underlying harder ground.[3] To supervise the work in progess, Telford sent his assistant, John Cargill, to Morpeth, since he had just completed similar duties in respect of the Over bridge. The Morpeth bridge was built by Thomas King and William Beldon and completed in 1831.

HEW 332

NZ 201 859

Sources

1. Sivewright W. J. *Civil engineering heritage: Wales and Western England.* Thomas Telford, London, 1986, 124–125.

2. Rickman J. (ed.) *Life of Thomas Telford*, 1838, 202.

3. Telford T. *Morpeth Bridge: Specification, 1829.* Northumberland Record Office: ZBS 2/30/3.

17. Whittle Dene Reservoirs

HEW 515

NZ 06 67

Before the formation of the Whittle Dean Water Company in 1845, the towns of Newcastle and Gateshead relied for their water supply on sources virtually within the towns' boundaries. To provide a supply of better quality and increased quantity the new company, with William George Armstrong its principal promoter, built a complex of impounding reservoirs at Whittle Dene, some 12 miles west of Newcastle.

The engineer responsible for the design of the reservoirs was James Simpson, who was responsible also for the Bristol Waterworks, and Robert Nicholson was appointed as resident engineer, presumably as Simpson's site visits were expected to be somewhat infrequent. Initially, three main reservoirs were built, principally to the south of the Military Road, the B6318. A feature of their design is that the reservoirs have at their heads—two streams are impounded—subsiding reservoirs, built to allow sediment to settle in them before the water passes into storage. The embankments are of earth construction with puddle clay cores and cut-offs; water is drawn from storage by means of cast iron pipes, valved

Whittle Dene
Reservoirs

NORTH EAST WATER PLC

in masonry forebays at their upstream ends. Built by Messrs Ridley and Atkinson, the reservoirs were completed in 1848.

Concurrent with reservoir construction was the laying to Newcastle of a major pipeline, a 24 in. diameter cast iron main approximately 12½ miles long; the pipes were supplied by the Company and were laid by Richard Butler. A house was built at Whittle Dene, both to provide accommodation for the reservoir keeper and to provide a room for directors' meetings; it was designed by John Dobson, a Newcastle architect.

Output from the reservoirs was soon found to be inadequate and further storage was provided; the Great Northern Reservoir was completed by Richard Cail in 1851 and the Great Southern by Benjamin Lawton in 1857. Both were to the designs of Nicholson and their completion brought total storage to 515 million gallons.

As a result of the reservoirs' flood overflows being grossly inadequate in respect of the Reservoirs (Safety Provisions) Act, 1930, they were modified under the direction of Stanley George Barrett; the contractors for this work were Ruddock & Meighan Ltd and Brims & Co. Ltd.

Sources

RENNISON R.W. *Water to Tyneside.* Newcastle and Gateshead Water Company, Newcastle upon Tyne, 1979.

RENNISON R.W. The impounding reservoirs of the Newcastle and Gateshead Water Company. *Trans. Newcomen Soc.,* 1982–83, **54**, 27–54.

18. Hallington Group of Reservoirs

As the consumption of water on Tyneside increased, the Newcastle and Gateshead Water Company—a change in name only from the earlier title—sought to increase supplies, first by forming an aqueduct to take water from the River Pont and then extending it into the Hallington district to tap streams there.

In 1863 John Frederic Bateman was appointed engineer to the Company and, under his direction, reservoirs were built in the Hallington area. The first of them was East Hallington, an earth embankment with a puddle clay core and cut-off. The maximum depth of water is 36 ft

HEW 1187

NY 978 764

25

and the capacity is 685 million gallons. In keeping with general practice, embankment slopes were 1 in 3 upstream and 1 in 2 downstream. Draw-off was by means of a 24 in. diameter pipe laid through the embankment and, somewhat surprisingly, valved only at its downstream end. Built by J.B. McGuire, the reservoir was completed in 1872.

HEW 1193

NY 941 780

The second stage of development was the building of Colt Crag and Little Swinburne reservoirs. Colt Crag was subject to geological problems; during construction, the 57 ft high embankment experienced slippage and it became necessary to provide upstream and downstream berms, thus widening the base of the embankment, making it more stable and reducing ground pressures. This problem also affected draw-off arrangements and had the effect, too, of inducing an inclination in the valve tower. Providing a capacity of 1068 million gallons, the reservoir was brought into use in 1884; the contractor was William Rigby of Worksop. The similar, but very much smaller, Little Swinburne Reservoir was completed by the same contractor in 1879. Both of them used towers and tunnels to accommodate draw-off pipes and valves; the tunnel at Colt Crag runs through the embankment, while at Little Swinburne it is in the natural ground on the reservoir's flank.

The final stage of development was the construction, by direct labour, of West Hallington reservoir, virtually identical to East Hallington. Drawings were prepared by John Reay Forster, employed full-time by the Company from 1863. This embankment, too, suffered from geological problems which were remedied in the same way.

After construction, Colt Crag was found to leak, a result of its location on limestone outcrops, and extensive remedial works became necessary. A cut-off trench was excavated to a maximum depth of 48 ft over a length of 650 yards and concrete was placed in the 6 ft wide trench, the first use by the Company of concrete for this application. It was completed in 1906.

When assessed under the Reservoirs (Safety Provisions) Act, 1930 the first three reservoirs—West Hallington has no catchment—were found lacking so far as flood disposal works were concerned and modifications were made to them between 1947 and 1951 under the direction of Stanley George Barrett.

Source

RENNISON R.W. The impounding reservoirs of the Newcastle and Gateshead Water Company. *Trans. Newcomen Soc.*, 1982–83, **54**, 27–54.

19. Catcleugh Reservoir

The last, and biggest, reservoir built by the Newcastle and Gateshead Water Company was Catcleugh, its catchment of some 10 000 acres extending to the Scottish border. Thomas Hawksley was appointed as engineer for its construction and he produced the initial designs, put in hand site investigations and established rain gauges to ascertain yields.

HEW 1186

NT 747 031

After his death in 1893 his son Charles became responsible, and under him a much enlarged reservoir of 2300 million gallons capacity was built by direct labour under the supervision of Charles Henzell. This reservoir exhibits all the features of the later phase of Victorian earth embankment dams: a concrete-filled cut-off trench to a maximum depth of 160 ft and some 600 yards long; a puddle clay core to a minimum thickness of 9 ft within the embankment; the well-compacted embankment itself, with an upstream slope of 1 in 3 and a downstream slope of 1 in 2½ and provision made for it to be raised; an outlet tunnel, almost 500 yards long and 12 ft 6 in. diame-

NORTH EAST WATER PLC

Tunnel outlet, Catcleugh Reservoir

27

ter, formed in the valley's side rather than within the embankment; and an overflow channel 210 ft wide at its upper end and 105 ft at its lower end, adequate even under the requirements of the Reservoirs Act, 1975. With a maximum depth of water of 78 ft, the reservoir was brought into use in 1905, its construction having taken ten years.

The reservoir, which supplies approximately 10 million gallons a day, forms only part of a comprehensive scheme designed by T. & C. Hawksley. A tunnel was built at Ryal, supplementing an earlier one; filters were built at Whittle Dene; mains were laid to carry water to the Tyneside conurbation; a pipe bridge was built at Swalwell to cross the River Derwent; a pumping station was constructed at Benwell; and two service reservoirs, one of them of brick vaulted construction, were provided at Byker, on the eastern outskirts of Newcastle.

Source

RENNISON R.W. The impounding reservoirs of the Newcastle and Gateshead Water Company. *Trans. Newcomen Soc.*, 1982–83, **54**, 27–54.

20. Kielder Viaduct

HEW 489

NY 632 924

Standing at the head of the Kielder reservoir, this viaduct formed part of the Border Counties Railway running from Hexham into Scotland and was completed in 1862. It comprises seven skewed spans of 40 ft with semicircular arches and its total length is 392 ft. The viaduct, presumably because of its proximity to the Duke of Northumberland's shooting lodge, was decorated with lozenge features in the spandrels and has battlemented parapets. Robert Nicholson had been responsible for the first part of the railway but, following his death in 1855, his nephew John Furness Tone became engineer, and it was under his direction that the viaduct was built by John Ridley and William Hutchinson.

With the construction of the reservoir, protection of the viaduct became necessary and the bases of the piers were cased in concrete with an exposed aggregate finish; at the same time, the bridge deck was waterproofed. These works were carried out by Wimpey Construction (UK) Ltd under the direction of R.T. James and Partners.

The viaduct is now the property of the Northumberland and Newcastle Society, having been closed to rail traffic.

Source

SEWELL G.W.M. *The North British Railway in Northumberland*. Martin Brooks, Braunton, 1992.

21. Seaton Sluice Harbour

The small natural Hartley Harbour, as it was then known, was protected in 1661 by a pier, constructed by Sir Ralph Delaval. Later, circa 1675, in an attempt to prevent or reduce the silting up of the harbour, sluicing arrangements were provided whereby water could be dammed at high tide and allowed to flow through the harbour at low tide, so removing silt from it. From this time the port became known as Seaton Sluice.

By the mid-18th century the harbour had become inadequate and, to remedy matters, Sir John Hussey Delaval, between 1761 and 1764, formed a new deepwater dock with coal staiths, accomplished by driving through a rock headland from the harbour to the sea. The new cut was 30 ft wide, 52 ft deep and almost 300 yards long. It

HEW 987

NZ 339 769

Seaton Sluice
Harbour before
1909.

CRASTER. HISTORY OF NORTHUMBERLAND. 1909

was provided with gates at each end, in effect providing a gated dock, the first in the North East.

In 1826 William Chapman prepared plans for a stone breakwater and wooden pier to the original north entrance to the harbour, together with a stone pier on the north side of the entrance to the Cut, but it is not known if his proposals were adopted. Improvements to the district's transport facilities and the cessation of mining at the Delavals' Hartley colliery as a result of an accident in 1862 led to the port's decline.

Source

HARTLEY J.R. Seaton Sluice: a survey of industrial development and decline in North East England. *Indust. Archaeol.*, 1977, **14**.

22. West Wylam Railway Bridge

Following the closure of the Wylam waggonway—the house of George Stephenson's birth may still be seen alongside it at Wylam—the Scotswood, Newburn and Wylam Railway was built to serve the north side of the Tyne. It left the Newcastle and Carlisle Railway at Scotswood and joined it again at West Wylam, where a wrought iron arch bridge with a suspended deck was built in 1876 to cross the River Tyne.

The bridge has three ribs spanning 240 ft and carried a double track. It was designed by William George Laws

HEW 19

NZ III 643

West Wylam
Railway Bridge

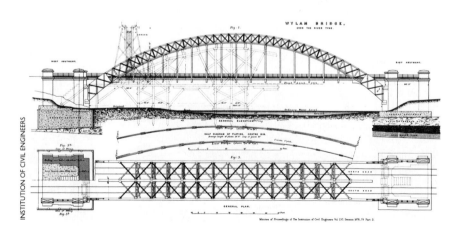

INSTITUTION OF CIVIL ENGINEERS

and his brother Hubert. Ironwork was the responsibility of Hawks Crawshay & Sons, of Gateshead, and the contractor for the masonry abutments was W. E. Jackson. The lattice ribs are 7 ft deep at the crown and 10 ft at the springing. Unlike the Tyne Bridge, the arch is built into the stone abutments, not pinned.

The railway closed in 1968 but the bridge has been preserved for pedestrian use.

Source

LAWS W.G. Railway bridge over the River Tyne at Wylam, Northumberland. *Min. Proc. Instn Civ. Engrs*, 1879, **56**, 262–274.

23. Ovingham Bridge

This bridge, completed in 1884 for the Ovingham Bridge Company, was designed by Hubert Laws and carries a roadway across the River Tyne. Principally single carriageway, two of its eight spans of 63 ft each are wide enough to form a passing place at the mid-point. The lattice girders are 5 ft 3 in. deep with top and bottom flanges 12 in. wide. An unusual feature is the method of support; trestles comprise double A-frames with 1½ in. diagonal ties and the piers consist of 10 in. diameter wrought iron tubes, fabricated from quadrants and bolted along their length. The girders sit on cast iron curved tubular caps which connect the inclined tubular supports.

HEW 708

NZ 086 636

For a road bridge, the trestle elements are almost certainly unique in form, although similar, but not identical, sections are to be found in two railway viaducts: Bennerley (1878)[1], and Meldon (1874 and 1879).[2]

Also to be seen at Ovingham (NZ 085 637) is a late 17th century packhorse bridge, 5 ft wide, with two segmental arches.

Sources

1. LABRUM E.A. *Civil engineering heritage: Eastern and Central England.* Thomas Telford, London, 1994, 27–28.

2. OTTER R.A. *Civil engineering heritage: Southern England.* Thomas Telford, London, 1994, 61–62.

24. Corbridge Bridge

HEW 995

NY 989 641

The present bridge at Corbridge, built in 1674, was the only one on the River Tyne to survive the disastrous flood which occurred on 17 November 1771; it was then recorded that the town's inhabitants, by leaning over the parapets, had been able to wash their hands in the water. Seven masonry spans varying from 44 to 64 ft are supported by massive piers and abutments and it is possible that they are built on Roman foundations. The south arch was rebuilt in 1829 and in 1881 the bridge was widened from 12 to 15 ft by supporting the parapets on corbels.

25. Hexham Bridge

HEW 536

NY 929 652

In 1756 a proposal for a bridge to cross the River Tyne at Hexham was made by John Smeaton. His design showed a four-span structure but there is some doubt as to the site considered. Some 20 years later, however, a bridge was built at Hexham with both John and William Gott involved; it was of seven spans, the largest of 70 ft. Its life was short as, with other bridges on the river, it was destroyed by the flood of November 1771.

Four years after the flood, a proposal was made for another bridge on a site near to that used earlier; the engineer was to be John Wooler. An investigation of the river bed was put in hand by Jonathan Pickernell and he found that the gravel bed of the river was underlain by running sand, an iron bar 45 ft long disappearing under hand pressure; understandably, the project was abandoned, only being revived after a lapse of another five years.

HEW 535

NY 941 647

This later project involved the construction of a bridge downstream of that which had failed. The bridge was designed by Smeaton and it was completed in 1781 under his and Pickernell's supervision. Initially, Smeaton had planned to build the central piers on undisturbed gravel in caissons, but as work proceeded it was found expedient to drive piles. It was, perhaps, this change, together with a restriction in the waterway, which led to the collapse of the bridge during a flood in March 1782.[1]

The bridge design produced by Smeaton showed fea-

J.G. JAMES

Hexham Bridge

tures very similar to those incorporated in his bridges at Coldstream, Perth and Banff, and the spans ranged from 37 to 52 ft. His original drawings showed abutments and bankside piers on piles with the bases of the other piers protected by 'beton', masonry placed so as afford protection.

After the bridge's collapse, Robert Mylne advised that it could be rebuilt and it was, in fact, probably completed in 1795.[2] The present structure occupies the site of Smeaton's bridge but is founded on a piled timber platform extending across the width of the river. The existing superstructure is identical to Smeaton's design; the roundels are purely a decorative feature.

Smeaton was deeply scarred by the failure of his bridge, which he did not live to see completed, and after its collapse he wrote that 'as it is out of my power to calculate the uttermost powers that Nature can collect, so it is out of my power to say what will absolutely stand against every possible violence'.[3]

33

Sources

1. RUDDOCK E.C. Foundations of Hexham Bridge. *Géotechnique*, 1977, **27**, 385–404.

2. LINSLEY S.M. Tyne crossings at Hexham up to 1795. *Archaelogia Aeliana*, Newcastle upon Tyne, 5th Series, 1994, **22**, 235–253.

3. SMEATON J. *Reports of the late John Smeaton, FRS*. Longman, London, 1812, **3**, 267–344.

26. Roman Bridges, Chollerford

HEW 761

NY 914 701

At the point where Hadrian's Wall crosses the River North Tyne stand the remains of two Roman bridges. On the line of the Wall, the remains of a bridge abutment and pier can be seen on the east bank of the river. The pier is part of an early bridge, thought to have been built at the same time as the wall. This structure comprised piers 9 ft 4 in. by 10 ft 4 in., with spans perhaps of some 15 ft.

Following construction of the bridge it would seem that the river changed course, leading to the second bridge being built circa A.D. 200, with its eastern abutment incorporating the older first pier within it. The later bridge consisted of piers with parallel sides 21 ft 6 in. in length and 16 ft wide, so leading to the conclusion that its deck width was greater than that of the earlier structure; its four spans were 35 ft 6 in. It is now thought that both bridges were of masonry arched construction.

A short distance upstream of the Roman remains is the more recent Chollerford bridge (NY 920 705). With five segmental arches varying from 41 to 56 ft, it was probably designed by John Fryer or John Wooler and built by William Johnson and Thomas Forster in 1775.

Sources

HOLMES S. The Roman bridges across the North Tyne near Chollerford. *Archaeologia Aeliana*, Newcastle upon Tyne, New Series, 1893, **16**, 328–338.

BIDWELL P.T. and HOLBROOK D. *Hadrian's Wall bridges*. Historic Buildings and Monuments Commission for England, London, 1989, 1–49.

27. Newcastle and Carlisle Railway

In 1776 proposals were made to build a canal along the Tyne valley and, although they were not implemented, the idea of a transport route between east and west coasts was to be later resurrected.

William Chapman was involved in one of the canal proposals and it was he, too, who was one of the engineers—the other was Josias Jessop—when the prospectus for a railway was published in 1825. Construction began in 1829 under the direction of Francis Giles and it was he who was responsible for the principal items of interest at the line's western end.

HEW 962

NZ 245 637 to NY 403 554

During the construction period, Giles was replaced by a committee of three, all engineers with a mining background: Benjamin Thompson, Nicolas Wood and George Johnson. Under their direction the 63 mile long railway was finally completed in June 1838, sections of it having been earlier brought into use.

Timber bridges designed by John Blackmore were used to cross the River Tyne at both Warden (NY 913 659) and Scotswood (NZ 198 638). That at Warden comprised five spans of 50 ft and that at Scotswood ten of 60 ft; both consisted of trusses supported on timber trestles.[1]

Because of concern about its condition in 1860, the Scotswood bridge was reported upon, independently, by three engineers, Giles, John F. Ure and John Furness Tone. All criticized its condition, Ure (Engineer to the Tyne Improvement Commission) writing on 16 April that it could take fire at any time. The bridge was subjected to loading tests on 19 May and was destroyed by fire the same afternoon, set alight by hot cinders from a crossing train.[2] A temporary bridge was built to replace it and a permanent one erected in 1868; Warden bridge was replaced in 1863.

At both its east and west ends the railway was progressively extended into the towns of Newcastle and Carlisle respectively, reaching the new Central Station in Newcastle in August 1850.

Sources

1. MACLEAN J. S. *The Newcastle and Carlisle Railway, 1825–1862*, Robinson, Newcastle upon Tyne, 1984.

2. BOYES J. H. Scotswood Bridge, Newcastle and Carlisle Railway. *J. Railway and Canal History Soc.*, Jan. 1961, **7**, No.1.

28. Lambley Viaduct

HEW 590

NY 675 584

Lambley Viaduct

The construction of the Alston Branch railway, from Haltwhistle to Alston, began in June 1849, the line forming part of the Newcastle and Carlisle Railway. The line incorporates 40 masonry bridges, the most notable being the Lambley Viaduct, crossing the River South Tyne.

R.W. RENNISON

The viaduct carried a single line of track at a height of 110 ft; it comprises nine semicircular masonry arches, each of 58 ft span, together with seven spans of 20 ft, all carried on tapering masonry piers. The piers penetrate gravel deposits and are founded on rock at depths of up to 30 ft. The engineer for the viaduct, opened in January 1852, was (Sir) George B. Bruce, and the contractors Rush and Lawton.

On the same line, crossing the Tyne near Haltwhistle, is another viaduct (NY 709 635) of six spans; four of its arches are skewed over the river and the piers are pierced by round-headed arches for an intended walkway.

Source

Newcastle Journal, 13 Sept. 1851.

29. Newcastle–Carlisle Road

As a result of transport problems in countering the 1745 Rebellion in Scotland, an Act of Parliament was obtained in 1751 for the construction of a new road between the towns of Newcastle and Carlisle, now known as the Military Road.

HEW 517

NZ 238 642 to NY 400 568

For most of its length of 56 miles the road follows, and in places lies upon, Hadrian's Wall, which formed a convenient quarry for construction materials. The width of the road was originally 27 ft between ditches and the actual carriageway was 16 ft wide; road formation was 15 in. thick at the crown and 5 in. at the edges. Bridges were 14 ft wide between parapets. Somewhat unusually, central government financed the road's construction, but thereafter it operated as a turnpike. Only one of the original 14 toll-houses remains, somewhat modified.

The line of the road was first surveyed by Dugal Campbell, Sub-Director of Engineers, and construction lasted from 1751 to 1757. For part of its length the surveyor in charge of the work, on a part-time basis, was John Brown, brother of landscape gardener 'Capability', and the work was undertaken by several contractors.

Source

LAWSON W. The construction of the military road in Northumberland, 1751–57. *Archaeologia Aeliana*, Newcastle upon Tyne, 5th Series, 1973, **1**, 177–193.

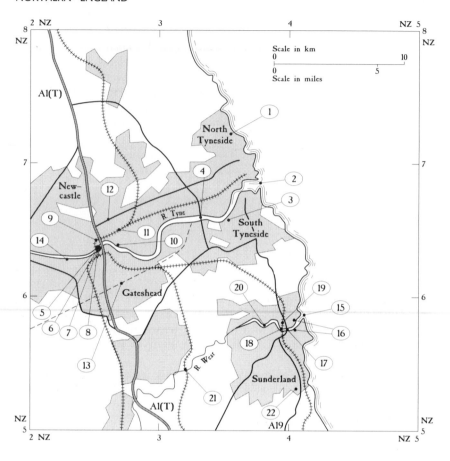

1 Spanish City, Whitley Bay

2 River Tyne Piers

3 Tyne Dock, Jarrow

4 Tyne Pedestrian and Cyclist Tunnels

5 Tyne Bridge, Newcastle

6 Swing Bridge, Newcastle

7 High Level Bridge, Newcastle

8 King Edward VII Rail Bridge, Newcastle

9 Central Station, Newcastle

10 Reinforced Concrete Warehouses, Newcastle

11 Ouseburn Viaducts, Newcastle

12 Armstrong Bridge, Newcastle

13 Bowes Railway

14 Dunston Staiths, Gateshead

15 River Wear Piers

16 Sunderland Docks

17 Wearmouth Bridge, Sunderland

18 Wear Rail Bridge, Sunderland

19 Monkwearmouth Station

20 Queen Alexandra Bridge, Sunderland

21 Victoria Viaduct, Penshaw

22 Ryhope Pumping Station

2. Tyne and Wear

The urban settlements based principally upon the tidal reaches of the rivers Tyne and Wear form the basis of the present county area. Coal was mined along the banks of both rivers as long ago as the 13th century, initially from outcropping seams and later by shallow mining. The invention of the steam engine resulted in the working of deeper pits and also led to the extension of mining into areas hitherto unworked. To enable the produce of the mines to be shipped to the principal markets, London and the east coast, a system of waggonways evolved; these were subsequently supplemented by colliery railways, some of them employing locomotive haulage.

With later improvements in steam engines came the mining of deeper seams and the subsequent migration of coal mining to the eastern parts of the county, together with the construction of railways, which were essential to transport the coal to the region's ports. In the North East, it was mainly the coal industry that brought early civil engineering into being.

Associated with the spread of railways was the construction of several notable bridges, among them the High Level Bridge, crossing the Tyne, and the Victoria Viaduct over the Wear; both were important in that they came to form links in the first railway between London and Edinburgh. With the railways—and largely for the transshipment of coal—came the development of ports and of coaling staiths, facilities provided both by the railway companies and by the governing bodies of the two rivers.

Sir William George Armstrong (1810–1900)

Both the Tyne Improvement Commission and the River Wear Commission were responsible for major river improvements, mainly in the latter half of the 19th century when extensive dredging took place and breakwaters were built.

During the same period, the shipbuilding and engineering industries flourished and with their expansion came considerable urban growth which, in turn, brought improved communications. At their peak, and as an example of the scale of Newcastle's expansion, Armstrong's enterprises came to employ no fewer than 20 000 men. Such expansion led to an increased need for water: the Newcastle and Gateshead and the Sunderland and South Shields water companies came into being in 1845 and 1852 respectively, although water had earlier been supplied by speculators. Similarly, gas and electricity came to be supplied by efficient and enterprising companies from 1817 and 1880 respectively.

The 20th century brought still further improvements in rail and road communications, together with several early reinforced concrete buildings, some extant. Although it is normal for Hennebique and Mouchel to be given credit for the introduction of reinforced concrete, it should be noted that a patent for this form of construction was taken out by William Boutland Wilkinson, a Newcastle plasterer, in 1865 and a small concrete house, now demolished, was actually built by him in Newcastle.

The Japanese battleship *Hatsuse* passing through the Swing Bridge, Newcastle, in 1899

FERROCONCRETE

I. Spanish City, Whitley Bay

Spanish City

The Spanish City at Whitley Bay is a minor version of Blackpool's Pleasure Beach. It was built by Whitley Bay Pleasure Gardens Ltd and its main point of interest, from a civil engineering aspect, is that it is a reinforced concrete structure, built in 1910 to provide a concert hall, restaurant, tea rooms and roof garden.

HEW 1995

NZ 355 725

The main façade of the building faces the sea over a length of 180 ft and the site is some 275 ft deep. The main feature of the complex is the dome, rising to a height of 73 ft above foundation level and having a clear span of 50 ft diameter. It is supported on reinforced concrete columns 46 ft high, in turn based on pad footings. The dome comprises a 5 in. thick reinforced concrete shell supported by twelve internal ribs 10 in. wide and 18 in. deep; the visible inner surface of the dome is decorative, masking the actual structure.

The architects for the buildings were Cackett and Burns Dick, perhaps with J. Coulson supervising the design, and L.G. Mouchel acted as structural consultants. The contractors were Davidson and Miller and work was completed in 1910.

Source

CACKETT J. T. and DICK B. Spanish City, Whitley Bay. *Ferro Concrete: a Monthly Review*, 1911, **2,** 168–175.

2. River Tyne Piers

Until 1850 the River Tyne was under the jurisdiction of Newcastle Corporation, the river's conservator since 1613. Under its control, river improvements were of a minor nature, leading to continuous complaints from the river's users. Principally as a result of pressure from shipowners based in North Shields, the Tyne Improvement Act, 1850 transferred control to a representative body, the Tyne Improvement Commission.

HEW 759

NZ 375 693 and NZ 374 678

Under its engineer, John Francis Ure, the Commission undertook an extensive programme of dredging while, as a consultant, James Walker was retained to prepare designs for the protection of the river's mouth. Walker's plans entailed the construction in masonry of two piers, the north 2100 ft long and the south 4200 ft. Philip John Messent was appointed resident engineer and construction began in 1855, the contractor being Benjamin Lawton.

Arrangement of staging and cranes used in construction of the South Pier

After Walker's death in 1862 his partners continued his work, submitting plans for longer, re-aligned and more substantial piers, now to be 2900 and 5400 ft long respectively, and extended into deeper water. Also in 1862, Lawton's contract was terminated and all subsequent work was carried out by the Commission under the direction of Messent. He was also responsible for the design of the cranes used to place concrete blocks weighing some 40 tons and cast on site, using concrete mixed

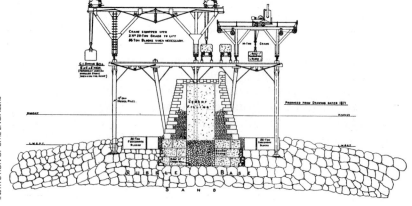

in a machine devised by him. It was not until 1895 that work was finished.

Soon after completion it was found that substantial damage had been sustained by the north pier as a result of storm action. Repairs were considered impracticable and plans for the pier's rebuilding were prepared. Messent's death in 1897 was attributed to the pier's failure. Rebuilding, to a different line, took place under the control of (Sir) John Wolfe Barry and Coode, Son and Matthews, Sir John Jackson Ltd being the contractor; work was completed in 1908.

Also of interest at the river mouth is the Groyne Lighthouse, built in 1882 and situated on a groyne to the south of the river's mouth, on the line of a pier first suggested by John Rennie in 1816. Leading lights also exist, built by Newcastle Trinity House in 1808 and first lit in 1810; designed by John Stokoe, a Newcastle architect, they replaced the old lights, used from 1727 and still extant.

HEW 1996

NZ 370 683

HEW 1997

**NZ 363 684
and NZ 360 685**

Sources

RENNISON R.W. The improvement of the River Tyne, 1815–1914. *Trans. Newcomen Soc.*, 1990–91, **62**, 113–142.

JOHNSON R.W. *The making of the River Tyne.* Walter Scott Ltd, Newcastle upon Tyne, 1895.

3. Tyne Dock, Jarrow

Resulting from an increase in coal traffic on the River Tyne, several proposals were made for the construction of docks, but only three came to be built. The first of them was the Northumberland Dock, the first task of the Tyne Improvement Commission after its formation in 1850. The dock was formed on a bight in the river at Hay Hole, where several waggonways discharged coal for shipment. Designed by John Plews, the dock had an area of 50 acres with a half-tide basin of 2½ acres but it has now been filled, with only the entrance visible.

The most significant of the river's docks was that built at Jarrow by the North Eastern Railway, formed by amalgamation in 1854. Since 1837, several schemes had been prepared, all associated with the Stanhope and Tyne Railway, which operated staiths nearby. The dock had an area of 50 acres with an entrance basin of 9½ acres; an

HEW 1998

NZ 354 658

PORT OF TYNE AUTHORITY

Tyne Dock,
Jarrow

80 ft wide entrance was provided, together with a lock having a 60 ft gate. Both provided a water depth of 24 ft. An inverted arch design was used for the underwater masonry at the entrance and it is interesting to note that Thomas Elliot Harrison acknowledged that his design incorporated features devised by Brunel for the North Dock on the Wear.

Three finger jetties with timber staiths were built at the south end of the dock, together with another fitted out for the removal of ballast. Begun in 1855, the dock was opened in March 1859; the resident engineer was Robert Hodgson. Construction was by Jackson, Bean and Gow and the gates were fabricated by Robert Stephenson & Co. with hydraulic machinery supplied by Sir W.G. Armstrong & Co.

The increasing size of ships using the river led to the dock's entrance being enlarged in 1894, so providing a depth of 32 ft. At its peak, in 1908, the dock trans-shipped some 7½ million tons of coal in the year, and it is reputed that, in total, more coal was shipped from it than from any other dock in Britain.

The third of the docks on the river is the 24 acre Albert

Edward, built on the north bank by the Commissioners under Ure and Messent; it was opened by the Prince of Wales in 1884 but was never financially successful.

Sources

HARRISON T.E. On the Tyne Docks at South Shields; and the mode adopted for shipping coal. *Min. Proc. Instn Civ. Engrs*, 1859, **18**, 490–524.

RENNISON R.W. The improvement of the River Tyne, 1815–1914. *Trans. Newcomen Soc.*, 1990–91, **62**, 113–142.

4. Tyne Pedestrian and Cyclist Tunnels

In 1797 Ralph Dodd proposed that a tunnel could be driven under the River Tyne between North and South Shields, thus reducing the journey for road traffic between the two towns from 18 miles to 400 yards. He estimated that, by employing techniques used in mining coal under the sea at Whitehaven, a 14 ft tunnel could be driven within 12 months for some £7000.

Many other schemes for improved cross-river communication were subsequently put forward but proposals for bridges met with strong opposition from the Admiralty. It was not until 1937 that an investigation of the problem by the County Councils of Northumberland and Durham led to firm plans being drawn up for a vehicular tunnel, together with two smaller ones, one for cyclists and one for pedestrians; the tunnel was to run between Howdon and Jarrow. Execution of the work was delayed by the outbreak of war in 1939 and it was not until 1946 that the scheme was finally sanctioned by Parliament. Work began the following year.

The pedestrian and cyclist tunnels are served by escalators and lifts on both sides of the river. On the south side, where the ground consisted of boulder clay overlying shales and sandstone, the construction of the escalator machinery chamber was carried out in a timbered excavation while the shaft was sunk by hand. Tunnelling for the 18 ft 6 in. diameter escalator tunnel, 10 ft 6 in. pedestrian tunnel and 12 ft cyclist tunnel was all carried out in free air without a shield.

On the north side, where water-bearing sands and gravels overlie the rock of the coal measures, the escalator

HEW 2010

NZ 330 658 to 329 662

45

machinery chamber was constructed in a sheet-piled cof-
ferdam. The shaft was sunk by kentledge and open grab-
bing until rock was reached at 75 ft; air locks were then
installed and the remainder of the shaft sunk by hand in
compressed air. Unexpectedly, the tunnel drives, also in
compressed air, soon ran into silts, sands and gravels
which lay in a buried channel beneath the existing river
bed. The open nature of the gravel led to high air losses
and, to prevent a 'blow', slag was deposited in the river,
some of it finding its way to the tunnel faces. So bad did
conditions become that a 7 ft diameter shield was used to
form a pilot tunnel through the worst section.

The tunnels' inverts are approximately 80 ft below
Ordnance Datum and they are each 900 ft long with cast
iron linings; the inclined escalator tunnels are 170 ft long,
and were the longest in Europe at the time of construction. Under the direction of Mott, Hay and Anderson as
consultants, Charles Brand & Son Ltd completed tunnelling in November 1949, but finishing work continued for
another year.

In the context of the history of civil engineering, it is of
interest to note that Robert Stephenson was born in a
house which formerly stood virtually on what is now the
north entrance to the tunnels.

Sources

DODD R. *A Report and Estimate on the projected Dry Tunnel....under the
River Tyne...*, North Shields, 1797.

PROSSER J.R. and GRANT P.A.St.C. The Tyne Tunnel 1: planning of the
scheme. *Proc. Instn Civ. Engrs*, 1968, **39**, 193–212.

5. Tyne Bridge, Newcastle

HEW 91

NZ 254 638

The Tyne Bridge, crossing the River Tyne between Newcastle and Gateshead, was opened by King George V on
10 October 1928. The bridge is a two-pin steel arch and at
the time of its construction was the longest of its type in
Britain, with a span between pins of 531 ft. The bridge
was designed by Mott, Hay and Anderson with, it would
seem, a significant contribution from (Sir) Ralph Free-
man, consultant to the contractors. It comprises two main
parabolic trusses with Warren bracing, each a maximum
of 20 ft 3 in. deep at mid-span. The trusses carry the 56 ft

UNIVERSITY OF NEWCASTLE SOCIETY OF ANTIQUITIES

wide road deck at a height of 93 ft above the river, giving a minimum clearance of 84 ft 6 in.

Tyne Bridges, Newcastle

The arches rise to a height of 170 ft above the 12 in. diameter pins, the latter backed by granite-faced towers, which are of little structural significance and which were intended to be used as warehouses. They, and the concrete bases supporting the pins, are founded on rock at depths of up to 60 ft below Ordnance Datum. The contractors were Dorman Long & Co. and the architect for the towers was R. Burns Dick.

Sources

'Verulam'. *The Structural Engineer*, 1989, **67**, No. 22, 402.

ANDERSON D. Tyne Bridge, Newcastle. *Min. Proc. Instn Civ. Engrs*, 1929–30, **230**, 167–202.

6. Swing Bridge, Newcastle

Newcastle's first bridge was built by the Romans and perhaps stood on the site now occupied by the Swing Bridge. Others followed, and after the medieval bridge had been destroyed in the flood of 1771, a nine-arched stone bridge was completed in 1781 by Robert Mylne. This bridge, however, permitted only the smallest of craft

HEW 92

NZ 253 637

to pass upstream and the expansion of works such as those of William George (later Lord) Armstrong at Elswick, above Newcastle, led to consideration being given to its replacement by a movable bridge.

The use of such a bridge had been first proposed by James Meadows Rendel in 1851 and a design for a bridge of the type later built had been prepared by Thomas Bryson, the Corporation's engineer, in 1864. The provision of the bridge was implemented by the Tyne Improvement Commission and its construction was completed in 1876. Under the overall direction of John Francis Ure, Engineer to the Commissioners, the bridge was designed and built by Sir W.G. Armstrong & Co. and comprises a single swinging section 278 ft 6 in. long, providing two openings each 103 ft wide, flanked by fixed spans of 107 and 88 ft.

The swinging section of the bridge consists of a girder 24 ft deep at its centre and 8 ft 3 in. at its ends, with a curved top boom. It provides a 22 ft wide roadway with two 8 ft wide footpaths. The swinging section carries a control house from which the hydraulic machinery is operated, the engines themselves being located in the central pier of the bridge.

The foundations comprise cast iron cylinders sunk to a rock base. The swinging section weighs about 1300 tons and is operated hydraulically. Originally, steam pumps charged the hydraulic accumulators which, in turn, powered the hydraulic engines, but in 1959 electric pumps replaced the steam-powered units.

Source

HOMFRAY S. G. *The Tyne Bridge*. Unpublished paper presented to the Tyne Engineering Society, 14 Feb. 1878.

7. High Level Bridge, Newcastle

The High Level Bridge is unusual in that it is a two-deck structure, carrying on its upper deck the lines of the former York, Newcastle and Berwick Railway, and on its lower a roadway between the towns of Newcastle and Gateshead. Before the final design was chosen, some 20 proposals had been made for a high level crossing, including designs by Samuel Brown, William Chapman,

Richard Grainger, Robert Stevenson, John Green, Isambard Kingdom Brunel and John Dobson. It was, however, through the influence of George Hudson and George Stephenson that the present crossing came into being, the Act of Parliament for its construction being passed in 1845.

The engineer for the bridge was Robert Stephenson, assisted by Thomas Elliot Harrison, and the first contract was let in July 1846. The bridge comprises six spans of 125 ft, and the rails are carried at a height of 120 ft above the river. The immediate masonry approaches are each 251 ft long. Each main span consists of four cast iron arch ribs and the rail deck is supported from them by means of cast iron columns; the road deck is at the level of the

HEW 22

NZ 252 637

R.W. RENNISON

Dean Street Arch

arch springing and is hung from rail level by wrought iron tension rods enclosed in cast box sections. The outward thrust of the main arches is counteracted by wrought iron tension chains at road level; they are visible from beneath the bridge.

The contractors for the ironwork were Hawks Crawshay & Sons, while the castings were provided by various local companies. The river piers and the northern approaches were built by Rush and Lawton and the southern by Wilson and Gibson; the resident engineer was Robert Hodgson. Nasmyth's steam hammer was used to drive the timber piles carrying the piers, one of the earliest instances of its use.

The bridge itself forms part of a most spectacular viaduct system approximately a mile in length. Among its bridges are two masonry skew bridges and the superb

HEW 334

NZ 251 639

HEW 36

NZ 250 638

St Nicholas
Street bridge

Dean Street Arch, with a span of 78 ft and a height of 80 ft, and three smaller arches flanking it on each side. Best viewed from the south, its original face—it was widened in 1894—shows a decorated frieze, unique to the system, while the main arch is multi-centred. Crossing St Nicholas Street is a 60 ft span iron bridge, its spandrels filled with lozenge bracing; it was cast by Abbot & Co. of Gateshead and it, too, was widened in 1894 by Walter

R.W. RENNISON

Scott & Co under the direction of Charles Augustus Harrison.

To enable rail traffic to cross the river before the completion of the permanent bridge, a timber structure was built and it was opened by George Hudson in August 1848. The permanent bridge was opened to traffic in August 1849, was ceremonially crossed by Queen Victoria in September of that year and became fully operational in February 1850.

Sources

RENNISON R.W. The high level bridge, Newcastle: its evolution, design and construction. *Trans. Newcomen Soc.* 1980–81, **52**, 180–207.

LAFFAN B.N. *Notes upon the high level bridge at Newcastle. Reports of the Commissioners of Railways for the year 1849.* Report from the Railway Commission, 1850, **12**, Appendix, 83–85.

8. King Edward VII Rail Bridge, Newcastle

Through running of trains on the east coast main line did not become possible until the King Edward Bridge had been completed in 1906. The bridge was designed by Charles Augustus Harrison and comprises two main spans, each of 300 ft, carrying four tracks across the Tyne with end spans of 191 and 231 ft respectively. The lattice girders of the bridge are of the double Warren type, 28 ft deep, and carry the tracks at a height of 112 ft above the river; they were built up in situ on trestles. Founded on rock throughout, the bridge's construction involved the sinking of caissons to a depth of up to 69 ft below high water. Above cut-water level the granite piers are built as triple shafts. The contractors were Cleveland Bridge and Engineering Co. Ltd.

Downstream is the Tyneside Metro bridge, designed by Fairhurst and Partners and opened by Queen Elizabeth II in November 1981; with a river span of 168 m (551 ft), it carries the Metro Rapid Transit System. Upstream is the post-tensioned concrete box Redheugh Bridge, designed by Mott, Hay and Anderson and opened in 1984. Two earlier bridges occupied its site. The first was a double Warren cable-stayed cantilever bridge with wrought iron tubular booms. Designed by (Sir)

HEW 256

NZ 247 633

HEW 925

NZ 245 631

Thomas Bouch, it was completed in 1870. It was succeeded in 1901 by a design comprising Pennsylvania trusses with principal spans of some 250 ft, similar to those of the earlier bridge; it was designed by Sandeman and Moncrieff.

Source

DAVIS F.W. and KIRKPATRICK C.R.S. The King Edward VII Bridge at Newcastle upon Tyne. *Min. Proc. Instn Civ. Engrs*, 1908, **174**, 158–221.

9. Central Station, Newcastle

HEWs 289 and 452

NZ 246 638

The Central Station is the work of John Dobson, a Newcastle architect. It was one of the first of many major stations with roofs having curved iron ribs of considerable span and was brought into use in 1850; those at York and Darlington date from 1877 and 1887 respectively. The Newcastle station was built jointly to serve the Newcastle and Carlisle and the York, Newcastle and Berwick railways, both terminating there.

The original roof comprises the three most northerly spans adjoining the station buildings. They form a large and impressive piece of architecture, enhanced by a portico added by Thomas Prosser in 1861. There are two lines of plain cast iron roof columns at 30 ft centres, with arcades of simple arched girders about 5 ft deep at the columns, with open spandrels. The arched roof ribs span some 62 ft and are at 10 ft centres with the centre span set 6 ft 6 in. higher than the other two. This is achieved by extending the columns upwards and incorporating shoes for the queen post timber and iron longitudinal trusses, which are boxed and panelled. The main roof ribs are simple made-up plate girders $9\frac{1}{2}$ in. deep and 6 in. wide, with 2 in. by 2 in. angles. The contractors for the ironwork were Abbot & Co. of Gateshead and, for the building, McKay and Blackstock.

Two further spans were added to the south side of the station by the architect, William Bell, in 1894 and are in keeping with the original work, although not quite so elegant. For his original design, Dobson had proposed a frontage even more impressive than the existing 600 ft long one, but the need for additional office space led him to change the design.

Sources

DOBSON J. Conditions and specification of the various works required to be done in the construction of the Newcastle upon Tyne Junction Railway Station, in T.L. Donaldson (ed.) *Handbook of Specifications*, Lockwood, London, 1859, **2**, 842–866.

GRUNDY J. *et al.* (Pevsner's) *The buildings of England: Northumberland.* Penguin, Harmondsworth, 1992, 455–457.

Central Station, Newcastle

10. Reinforced Concrete Warehouses, Newcastle

In 1892, François Hennebique, formerly a public works contractor, introduced a system of combining steel with concrete to form *beton armé*, reinforced concrete. His ideas were developed further by Louis Gustave Mouchel, who brought its use to Britain. His first important application was Weavers Mill, Swansea, completed in 1898 but now demolished.

Several similar structures were commissioned for the Co-operative Wholesale Society and a warehouse, completed in 1901, still stands on Newcastle Quayside. It was originally intended to be founded on piles, but Mouchel instead used a raft, so halving foundation costs. Built by Brims & Co., the building is completely of reinforced concrete, its plan area 124 ft by 90 ft, with columns at approximately 15 ft centres; it is eight storeys high. Col-

HEW 979

NZ 255 640

Co-operative
Wholesale
Society
warehouse,
Newcastle

R.W. RENNISON

umn sizes vary from 29 in. square at basement level to
8 in. square at the upper floor, added in 1909, at which
time a 30 ft span vaulted arch roof 3 in. thick was added.

HEW 2000

NZ 270 636

Also to be seen on the Quayside is a more recent
reinforced concrete building, Spillers Mill. In traditional
flour mills, fire had been a hazard and reinforced concrete
brought advantages in this respect. The structure comprises a set of 84 grain silos which contain approximately
34 000 tons, together with a mill building. The silos,
almost 120 ft high, occupy a site 220 ft by 90 ft and the

54

mill one of 280 ft by 80 ft. The silos were formed as a cluster of vertical bins, each approximately 14 ft square with reinforced concrete walls generally 6 in. thick. In a form of construction perhaps then unusual, the bins were slip-formed, the major part of their height being completed in 21 days.

The mill building is of twelve storeys with reinforced concrete columns and beams; it has floors of 4 in. thick Columbian pine with maple strip finish. Part of the mill building was demolished in 1987 and replaced by a warehouse. Both silos and mill are founded on bearing piles 18–45 ft long, each designed to take a loading of 60 tons. Completed at the end of 1937, the mill was designed by Oscar Faber and built by Richard Costain Ltd.

Sources

MOUCHEL L.G. *Mouchel–Hennebique Ferro-Concrete*. Mouchel, London, 1921, **42,** 83 and 143.

FABER O. Some recent industrial buildings. *Structural Engineer*, 15 Nov. 1937, 466–481.

11. Ouseburn Viaducts, Newcastle

Crossing the Ouseburn, which flows into the Tyne approximately a mile to the east of the centre of Newcastle, are three notable viaducts, one of them new. The earliest is the Ouseburn Viaduct, which now forms part of the   **HEW 193** east coast main line, but which was built for the Newcastle and North Shields Railway and completed in 1839.   **NZ 262 647**

The engineer for the railway was Robert Nicholson, but the viaduct was designed by John Green. What is of interest is that the viaduct, now of wrought iron, was originally built in laminated timber arch form, in outline almost identical to its present shape. It comprises five spans, each of 131 ft centres, the arches themselves being of 116 ft span with a rise of 32 ft 6 in.; the height of the track above foundations is 108 ft and the total length of the structure is 918 ft.[1] The original viaduct was built by Messrs Welch and the iron replacement of 1869 by the Weardale Iron and Coal Company. Two additional tracks were provided by (Sir) Walter Scott in 1885. The original viaduct was reputedly one of the earliest of such structures in Britain and it is of interest to note that Green suggested later that the Tyne be spanned in a similar manner. The fact that timber was quite widely used in structures of this type is now overlooked, but its use was adopted by several engineers of the period.[2]

HEW 2001

NZ 262 646

Also crossing the Ouseburn is the Byker Bridge, built for a company of that name by Scott and completed in 1879.[3] Robert Hodgson was the designer and, as a result, it is perhaps not surprising that it has the appearance of a railway viaduct. Problems were encountered with its foundations and eventually iron cylinders were used to support some of the piers. The bridge has 14 spans of 60 ft with eight spans of 25 ft, now filled, at its eastern end and its piers taper slightly to the semi-elliptical arches; it is built entirely of brick and rises to a height of 95 ft above the river. The bridge was widened in 1902 by introducing cantilevered footpaths and was further improved and strengthened in 1985 when post-tensioned concrete beams were incorporated to enable new footways and crash barriers to be provided.

HEW 2009

NZ 262 646

The third of the Ouseburn crossings is the viaduct built for the Tyneside Metro system. In plan S-shaped, the multi-span structure crosses the actual valley in six spans of up to 226 ft, rising at its eastern end to pass over the Byker Bridge roadway. It is the first structure of this type in Britain to have been built using cantilevered construction with precast concrete sections having epoxy resin glued joints. It is a most graceful structure and carries a double standard-gauge track at an elevation of more than 100 ft, its piers flared out at their bases, so permitting the web of the double I-section to be cut away. Designed to resist the centrifugal forces resulting from the curved alignment, the piers are based on piled foundations. The viaduct was designed by Ove Arup and Partners and completed by John Mowlem & Co. Ltd in 1979.[4]

HEW 194

NZ 316 667

Similar in form to the Ouseburn Viaduct is that crossing Willington Gut, also on the former N&NSR line. It has seven spans of up to 128 ft and a height of 82 ft; also designed by Green, it was built by Messrs Robson. Its timber structure was also replaced by iron in 1869.

Sources

1. GREEN B. On the arched timber viaducts on the Newcastle and North Shields Railway. *Min. Proc. Instn Civ. Engrs*, 1846, **5**, 219–232.

R.W. RENNISON

2. Booth L.G. Laminated timber arch bridges. *Trans. Newcomen Soc.*, 1971, **44**, 1–21.

Willington Viaduct

3. *Byker Bridge Company: Board Minutes.* Tyne and Wear Archives 561/45.

4. Smyth W.J.R. *et al.* Tyne and Wear Metro: Byker Viaduct. *Proc. Instn Civ. Engrs*, 1980, **68**, 701–718.

12. Armstrong Bridge, Newcastle

At the time of its construction, the Armstrong Bridge was almost certainly unique in that it was designed to provide complete articulation and so obviate any problems which might arise as a result of mining subsidence. It was designed and built by Sir W.G. Armstrong & Co. and was completed in April 1878, the major part of its cost having been met by Sir William Armstrong. It provides a high-level roadway—with a maximum height of 65 ft—over the Ouseburn and Jesmond Dene, the property of Armstrong which was given by him to the town of Newcastle.

HEW 985

NZ 264 662

The bridge comprises eight wrought iron lattice spans of approximately 69 ft, providing a total length of 553 ft with a width of 25 ft. The girders were carried by wrought iron square section box columns, in pairs and cross-braced with adjustable wrought iron ties. Each column is supported on a rocker bearing, in turn based on a masonry pier, and there is a sliding movement joint in the girders at mid-span; it is built-in at the abutments. The masonry contractors were Messrs W.E. and F. Jackson.

The bridge was threatened with demolition in the 1970s, but it was eventually agreed that it should be reprieved and in 1983 the deteriorating columns were replaced, quite sympathetically, by steel universal sections; it is now restricted to foot and cycle traffic.

Source

In Trust: The Armstrong Bridge. Tyne and Wear Industrial Monuments Trust, Newcastle, Nov. 1984, 12.

13. Bowes Railway

The use of waggonways to carry coal from colliery to ship began in the North East at the beginning of the 17th century; they ran generally from higher ground to the navigable stretches of the rivers Tyne and Wear, principally in a north–south direction. From the late 18th century, the waggonways were able to adopt gravity inclines and rope haulage, although horses were widely used until they were replaced by locomotives. On reaching the river, the coal was stored on riverside platforms, or staiths, until it could be transferred to keels, barges of some 21 tons capacity. It was then taken to ships which were often forced to lie in the lower reaches of the river.

In an effort to minimize the river stage of the transport process, several colliery railways were built, tending to run towards the east, where they carried coal direct to ship. Examples of such railways were the Newbottle railway of 1815, leading to the Wear at Sunderland; the Hetton colliery railway, laid out by George Stephenson and opened in 1822 using locomotive haulage over part of its route to Sunderland; the Pelaw Main railway to the Tyne, planned by Benjamin Thompson in 1809 and incorporating rope haulage; the Pontop and Jarrow (later the Bowes) railway leading to the Tyne at Jarrow; and the Brunton and Shields railway of 1826, reaching the Tyne at Wallsend. Steam locomotives, fixed engine haulage and self-acting inclines were adopted for the movement of traffic.

The route of the Bowes railway was surveyed in 1822 by John Buddle, later to be involved in the founding of Seaham Harbour, and under George Stephenson its first section of 6½ miles from Mount Moor to Jarrow was opened in 1826. It included four rope-worked inclines, together with locomotive haulage. The line was later extended and by 1854 totalled some 14 miles, using all of the foregoing methods of haulage. In 1851 it came under the control of John Bowes and Partners, of which concern Charles Mark Palmer was managing partner and involved in the establishment at Jarrow of a shipyard. The railway closed in 1974, but a section of it (approached at NZ 285 588) has been preserved by the Bowes Railway Company Ltd, which arranges demonstrations of rope working.

HEW 1029

NZ 317 659 to 170 555

Source

The Bowes Railway. Tyne and Wear Industrial Monuments Trust, Newcastle upon Tyne, 1975.

14. Dunston Staiths, Gateshead

The first stage of the timber staiths for the trans-shipment of coal at Dunston was opened by the North Eastern Railway in 1893. They are situated about a mile upstream of the Newcastle bridges and occupy a site on which similar, but smaller and more primitive, staiths had been located from perhaps the 17th century.

HEW 2003

NZ 235 626

Before the improvement of the River Tyne had been put in hand, there had been a tendency for colliery railways such as the Bowes railway to be built so as to avoid the deficiencies of the river itself, all of the railways discharging at points between Newcastle and the sea. Such were the improvements made to the river by the Tyne Improvement Commission, following its formation in 1850, that by the last decade of the 19th century it was possible for the North Eastern Railway to build staiths on an up-river site rather than expand its facilities at Tyne Dock. The success of this installation resulted in a further set of staiths being built immediately adjoining the earlier structure, on the landward side, and a basin being excavated from the river bank to allow ships to load from both sides of the extended structure.

PORT OF TYNE AUTHORITY

Dunston Staiths   The staiths comprise timber piles driven into the river bed, on top of which are 13 in. by 13 in. pitch pine braced trestles at approximately 17 ft 6 in. centres; there are 98 trestles giving a total length of approximately 1730 ft. Rail tracks are carried on a timber deck and chutes were used to discharge coal directly from waggon to ship.

These staiths, built while Charles Augustus Harrison was Chief Divisional Engineer to the railway company, were the last timber staiths to operate on the Tyne. The later installation was damaged by fire in the 1970s and was later dismantled, but the first structure survives.

Sources

RENNISON R.W. The Improvement of the River Tyne, 1815–1914. *Trans. Newcomen Soc.* 1990–91, **62**, 113–142.

Dunston dusts off coal past. *New Civil Engineer*, 26 Nov.1987, 41–43.

15. River Wear Piers

With the River Tyne, the Wear was traditionally one of the principal outlets for coal from the region. Unlike the Tyne, however, the Wear had been controlled from 1717 by a far-seeing and active group of commissioners who had expended no little money on the improvement of the port of Sunderland. Under a succession of able engineers, it had been progressively improved but, nevertheless, it became necessary to provide more substantial piers and as a result new north and south piers were built between 1804 and 1842.

Following the construction of docks at Sunderland and the absorption of the Sunderland Dock Company by the River Wear Commission in 1859, the views of Sir John Coode were sought on the provision of new breakwaters. Their construction began in 1868 under the control of Henry Hay Wake, Engineer to the Commission.

Both north and south piers, or breakwaters, are of masonry-faced concrete construction, founded on concrete placed in jute bags which, when filled, weighed from 52 to 116 tons each; the concrete bags were placed so as to form a foundation for the masonry 18 in. above low water. The north pier, built of blocks weighing 43 tons, is 2880 ft long and the roundhead consists of a steel caisson 101 ft by 66 ft filled with concrete; on it was placed a lighthouse. The south pier is 2666 ft long, the two piers forming an entrance 775 ft wide. The north pier was built between 1885 and 1903 and the south between 1891 and 1914, being then virtually abandoned as a result of the outbreak of war. Both piers were built by direct labour.

HEW 1860

NZ 41 58

Sources

MURRAY J. On the progressive improvement of Sunderland Harbour and the River Wear. *Min. Proc. Instn Civ. Engrs*, 1847, **6**, 256–283.

RENNISON R.W. *The development of the North East Coal Ports, 1815–1914.* University of Newcastle upon Tyne, PhD thesis, 1987.

16. Sunderland Docks

As a result of the expansion of the coal trade it became necessary to provide docks on the River Wear in order to accommodate the increase in shipping. Staiths had first been provided on the river itself, some miles upstream from Sunderland but, although the colliery railways which had been completed circa 1820 had brought coal into the town, it was still considered that docks should be provided. Ralph Dodd had first reported on their need in 1794, but it was not until 1834, when a royal charter was obtained by Sir Hedworth Williamson, that work on the North Dock was put in hand.

HEW 1861

NZ 407 585

The engineer was Isambard Kingdom Brunel and under him a dock of 6 acres was completed, although it was the smallest of the three proposals he had made. He had intended to bridge the river by means of a two-deck suspension bridge to bring more trade to the dock, but this part of his scheme was not executed, an outcome perhaps fortunate in view of the fate of the similar bridge at Stockton. With a 48 ft wide entrance the dock was completed by Joseph Welch in 1837.

HEW 1862

NZ 410 578

The Sunderland Dock Company was formed in 1846, the year in which George Hudson, the company's first chairman, was elected to represent the town in Parliament. The construction of a dock on the south side of the river was immediately put in hand with John Murray, formerly Engineer to the Commission, as its engineer; Robert Stephenson acted as consultant for the Parliamentary proceedings, but thereafter was little involved. The dock was of 19 acres and an unusual feature of its design,

Sunderland Docks

AEROFILMS

although not immediately provided, was its south entrance, leading directly to the sea, in addition to the river gates; the sea entrance was built when the dock was extended in 1856. Further extensions and deepening took place under Thomas Meik and Henry Hay Wake and the water surface totalled 51 acres by 1904. By then, the entrance had been enlarged from its original 60 ft width and 20 ft depth to 70 ft and 30 ft respectively.

Contractors for the original work were John Craven & Sons, with Hawks Crawshay & Sons responsible for the gates; for the first extension, the major part of the work was undertaken by direct labour with gates by Butler & Co. and hydraulic machinery by W.G. Armstrong & Co. Initially, sluicing arrangements had been provided at the sea entrance, but this feature was dispensed with when, in 1904, a new lock replaced the basin there, this work being carried out by Sir John Jackson. Providing for general cargoes in addition to coal, the dock was equipped with two warehouses, one designed by John Dobson in 1856 and the other by Meik in 1866; both were demolished in 1992.

Sources

MURRAY J. On the progressive construction of Sunderland docks. *Min. Proc. Instn Civ. Engrs*, 1856, **15**, 418–455.

Archive material held by University of Bristol Library.

17. Wearmouth Bridge, Sunderland

Until the end of the 18th century, when the iron bridge at Sunderland was built, the only means of crossing the River Wear downstream of Chester-le-Street was by ferry. The first Sunderland Bridge was sanctioned by Act of Parliament and opened in 1796. The bridge was planned by Rowland Burdon and, although there are many attributions regarding its design, it was cast by Walkers of Rotherham and built under the supervision of Thomas Wilson.

HEW 528

NZ 397 574

The bridge, unlike the earlier one at Coalbrookdale, was made up of relatively small castings, 105 of them making up each of the six ribs; the castings were held together by means of wrought iron ties and the ribs spaced apart by tubes. With a span of 236 ft and a width of 32 ft, its construction was completed without undue interruption to river traffic.

Over the years the bridge deteriorated and the advice of Robert Stephenson was sought; then in poor health, he delegated much of the remedial work to his assistant, George Henry Phipps. The bridge was dismantled, leaving only the ribs standing, and three wrought iron box girders were inserted between pairs of ribs. The bridge was widened to 41 ft 6 in. and its approach gradients substantially reduced; this work was completed in 1858.

HEW 762

NZ 397 574

The present Wearmouth Bridge, a steel three-pin arch of 375 ft span, was built without interrupting either river or road traffic and, following completion, the old structure was demolished. The present bridge, without the towers used at Newcastle and using rocker bearings rather than pins, carries the roadway at a height of 93 ft. It was designed by Mott, Hay and Anderson, built by Sir William Arrol & Co. Ltd and was opened by the Duke of York on 31 October 1929.

Wearmouth Bridge, Sunderland, under construction in 1928

Sources

JAMES J.G. *The Cast Iron Bridge at Sunderland, 1896.* Newcastle upon Tyne Polytechnic, 1986.

T. H. NICHOLSON

GROVES G.L. The New Wearmouth Bridge, Sunderland. *Min. Proc. Instn Civ. Engrs*, 1929–30, **230**, 144–166.

18. Wear Rail Bridge, Sunderland

The Brandling Junction Railway, with one section running from Newcastle to the Wear, originally terminated at Monkwearmouth, but in 1879 the line was extended southwards into Sunderland, crossing the River Wear by means of a bow-string/Vierendeel girder bridge designed by Thomas Elliot Harrison.

HEW 728

NZ 396 574

The wrought iron bridge has a clear span of 300 ft and the twin girders are 42 ft deep at their centres. Verticals in the bowstring are placed at 20 ft centres and are stiffened at their junctions by means of curved bracings, imparting to the structure the effect of elliptical piercing through the girders; the clearance above the river is 86 ft. The contractors for the ironwork were Hawks Crawshay & Sons. There are three masonry arches of 25 ft span at each end, built by John Waddell.

Source

TOMLINSON W.W. *The North Eastern Railway*. Longmans Green, London, 1914, 685.

19. Monkwearmouth Station

This station stands on the north bank of the River Wear. It was originally designed as the terminus of the Brandling Junction Railway, but when the line came to be extended into Sunderland in 1879 it was converted for through running.

The station at Monkwearmouth was designed by Thomas Moore, a Sunderland architect, and was opened in June 1848, at which time George Hudson was Member of Parliament for the town, perhaps accounting for the relatively lavish design. The single-storey classical building includes a two-storey central Ionic portico and pediment with Doric end pavilions. Contractors for the masonry were Tone & Sons, for the joinery John Patterson, and for the ironwork Hawks Crawshay.

HEW 290

NZ 396 577

In 1973 the station buildings were opened as a museum, mainly housing railway material.

R.W. RENNISON

Monkwearmouth
Station

Source

PEVSNER N. *The buildings of England: County Durham.* Penguin, London, 1983, 468.

20. Queen Alexandra Bridge, Sunderland

HEW 2002

NZ 382 579

More than half a century after the completion of the Newcastle High Level Bridge another two-deck bridge came to be built, to provide a crossing of the River Wear. Built jointly by the North Eastern Railway and Sunderland Corporation, it comprises three spans of 200 ft with a river span of 300 ft, providing headroom of 85 ft at high water.

Linville-type lattice girders generally 30 ft deep—42 ft at the river span—carry a roadway at a lower level with the rail tracks above; the main girders are at 32 ft centres. The abutments and piers are of Norwegian rock-faced granite and their foundations extend to a maximum depth of almost 80 ft below high water.

Built by Sir William Arrol & Co. Ltd without interference to shipping, the bridge was opened by the Earl of Durham on 10 June 1909, having taken four years to build; the designer was Charles Augustus Harrison. The upper deck was closed in 1921 and the rail approaches removed in 1985.

Source

BUSCARLET F.C. The Queen Alexandra Bridge over the River Wear. *Min. Proc. Instn Civ. Engrs*, 1909–10, **182,** 59–131.

21. Victoria Viaduct, Penshaw

The major work of the Durham Junction Railway, the Victoria Viaduct was completed on 28 August 1838, providing a crossing of the River Wear. The viaduct, which came to form part of the first main line between Darlington and Gateshead in 1844, comprises four main arches of 100, 160, 144 and 100 ft span, with three spans of 20 ft at each end. The total length of the structure is 811 ft and the tracks are carried at a height of 120 ft above the river; the viaduct's overall width is 23 ft 3 in. Foundations reached rock at depths of up to 40 ft below flood level.

An iron bridge was first proposed by John Green, but his design was rejected in favour of the masonry structure designed by James Walker, based on Trajan's bridge at Alcantara where spans of 98 ft carry the roadway at a height of 170 ft. The small end spans did not form part of Walker's design, but were probably the result of amend-

HEW 156

NZ 320 546

Victoria Viaduct, Penshaw

ments made by Thomas Elliot Harrison, Engineer to the Durham Junction Railway. Incorporating stone from the nearby Penshaw quarry, the bridge was built by John Gibb & Son of Aberdeen.

Source

BREMNER R.D. Account of the Victoria Bridge, erected across the River Wear, on the line of the Durham Junction Railway. *Min. Proc. Instn Civ. Engrs*, 1843, **2**, 97–99.

22. Ryhope Pumping Station

Ryhope Pumping Station

The Sunderland and South Shields Water Company was formed in 1852, although water had been supplied to the

two towns much earlier. As a result of a report submitted by Thomas Hawksley in 1860, pumping stations were built at Cleadon in 1863, Ryhope in 1869 and Dalton in 1877; all of them abstracted underground water, unlike the neighbouring Newcastle and Gateshead Water Company, which relied at that time on both impounding reservoirs and river pumping.

The pumping station at Ryhope, now in the care of the Ryhope Engines Trust, was constructed between 1865 and 1869, a feature of its construction being the use of one of the engines to dewater the well during its sinking. The main well, 15 ft in diameter, was sunk to a depth of 253 ft while the other, an ellipse, reached 140 ft.

HEW 180

NZ 404 525

Above the well were placed two compound beam engines built in Newcastle by R. & W. Hawthorn, each having a pump stroke of 10 ft 8 in. and cylinders 23½ in. and 45 in. diameter; with a steam pressure of 30 pounds per square inch, they were capable of pumping 40 000 gallons of water per hour. The boiler house initially contained six Cornish boilers, but they were replaced by Lancashire boilers in 1908.

Built by William Jackson of Newcastle to Hawksley's design, the works form a distinctive example of the Victorian Gothic style. The station is operated by the Trust on a regular basis, principally at holiday weekends, when the engines may be seen in steam.

Source

LINSLEY S.M. *Ryhope Pumping Station. A history and description*. Ryhope Engines Trust, Newcastle upon Tyne, 1973.

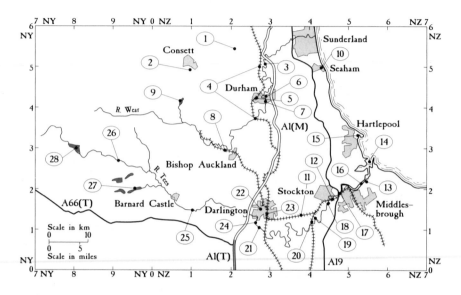

1   Causey Arch, Tanfield
2   Hownes Gill Viaduct, Consett
3   Chester New Bridge
4   Chester-le-Street and Croxdale Viaducts
5   Durham Viaduct and Station
6   Gilesgate Station, Durham
7   Durham City Bridges
8   Bridge near Escomb, Bishop Auckland
9   Tunstall Reservoir
10 Seaham Harbour
11 Stockton and Darlington Railway
12 Tees Suspension Bridge, Stockton
13 Middlesbrough Dock
14 River Tees Breakwaters

15 Hartlepool Docks
16 Middlesbrough Transporter Bridge
17 Newport Lift Bridge, Middlesbrough
18 Victoria Bridge, Stockton
19 Yarm Bridge
20 Yarm Viaduct
21 Blackwell Bridge, Darlington
22 Darlington North Road Station
23 Darlington Bank Top Station
24 Darlington Pumping Station
25 Whorlton Bridge
26 Wynch Bridge
27 Hury and Blackton Reservoirs
28 Cow Green Reservoir

3. County Durham and Cleveland

County Durham lies mainly between the rivers Tyne and Tees, with Cleveland embracing the industrial areas of Middlesbrough, Stockton and Hartlepool, together with the former north-eastern area of Yorkshire. To the west are the Pennines and the underlying strata dip generally from west to east. Present in these rocks are deposits of coal and ironstone, but the major coal deposits, and the last to be worked, lie to the east, protected by a layer of magnesian limestone. The expansion of coal mining, an industry which has now ceased, led to a seven-fold increase in population during the 19th century.

Coal had been first shipped from the Northumberland and Durham coalfield through the rivers Tyne and Wear, but the mining of deeper seams in the eastern part of Durham—a result of the winning of Hetton colliery in 1822—led to the creation of new outlets. Middlesbrough was founded by the Stockton and Darlington Railway (S&DR), Hartlepool was developed by two rival companies and Seaham built privately by the Marquess of Londonderry. With the establishment of these ports came a proliferation of railways, both for the export of coal and also for the transport of iron ore and limestone. Most of them were absorbed into the North Eastern Railway following its formation in 1854 and the S&DR lasted as a separate entity only until 1863.

At the time of the completion of the S&DR in 1825, built principally for the carriage of minerals, the only ports on the River Tees

INSTITUTION OF CIVIL ENGINEERS

Thomas Elliot Harrison (1808–88)

71

were Stockton and Yarm. The extension of the railway to Middlesbrough in 1830 was largely responsible for the subsequent rapid growth of that town, which soon became, with Tyneside, a major centre of industry in the North East. From 1850 onwards, the development of Teesside was aided by the exploitation of ironstone in the Cleveland district, in turn leading to the establishment of ironworks at Middlesbrough; later, the building of a vast complex of chemical works took place at Billingham.

The expansion of Teesside led to vast river improvements being made by the Tees Conservancy Commission, while the growth in population led to the construction of a complex of reservoirs in the upper valley of the Tees so as to supply water for both domestic and industrial purposes. The industry of the Tees was perhaps unique in Britain in the quantities of untreated water used.

HUTCHINSON. THE HISTORY AND ANTIQUITIES OF THE COUNTY PALATINE OF DURHAM. 1794

1. Causey Arch, Tanfield

The mining of coal in County Durham first took place along the banks of the River Tyne, but as the mines above the water table became worked out coal mining began in areas more remote from the river, made possible by the construction of waggonways to convey the coal to the river for shipment. One of the waggonways so formed was that running some five miles from Tanfield to the Tyne at Dunston, a mile upstream from Newcastle; crossing the Causey Burn, the Arch formed part of it. Built in 1727 by the mason Ralph Wood, it was commissioned for the Grand Allies. Claimed to be the fifth largest span of masonry bridges in Britain, it remained the largest stone span for 30 years, its nearest rival being the road bridge at Twizel. The arch is 35 ft high from springing to soffit with a span of 105 ft and a height of 80 ft; it carried a double track railway.

HEW 89

NZ 201 559

The bridge is now the property of Durham County Council and has been repaired, first between 1977 and 1982 and again in 1988. When first built, such was its novelty and importance that the bridge, together with the massive embankment adjoining it, was often visited as one of the great feats of engineering.

R.W. RENNISON

Opposite: Wynch
Bridge in 1794

Left: Causey
Arch, Tanfield

73

Sources

STROUD A. Invisible mending. *Concrete Quarterly*, 1988, Autumn, 26–27.

1725 onwards: a guide to the Tanfield Railway. Newcastle upon Tyne, no date, 1–2.

2. Hownes Gill Viaduct, Consett

HEW 157

NZ 096 491

The Hownes Gill Viaduct stands on the line of what was the Stanhope and Tyne Railway, opened in 1834. In 1841 the western section of the line was sold to the Derwent Iron Company, which was based at Consett, and eventually it came under the control of the Stockton and Darlington Railway. To cross the ravine at Hownes Gill the railway company worked a double incline system to cross the valley, a method which became a severe bottleneck. As a result of the inconvenience so caused, the Stockton and Darlington Railway decided to replace the inclines with a viaduct, the Engineer for its design being (Sir) Thomas Bouch, employed by the contractor, John Anderson.

Hownes Gill
Viaduct

Bouch's designs were submitted to Robert Stephenson for his approval, and the latter recommended that inverted

R.W. RENNISON

arches be used under the five central piers to reduce ground loading. The piers are recessed to reduce loading still further. The viaduct, with its twelve arches of 50 ft span and built of firebrick, is a most graceful structure and reaches a height of 150 ft above the valley floor, its 750 ft length formerly carrying a single track railway. It is now a public footpath.

Source

CUDWORTH W. The Hownes Gill viaduct on the Stockton and Darlington Railway. *Min. Proc. Instn Civ. Engrs*, 1862, **22**, 44–57.

3. Chester New Bridge

The bridge was built as a means of communication between Chester-le-Street and Sunderland and was the lowest crossing on the River Wear, excluding ferries, until Sunderland Bridge was completed in 1796. The bridge dates from the 14th century and comprises four spans of 26, 32, 32 and 26 ft; all the arches are pointed with five soffit ribs, and the bridge has a width of 16 ft 6 in. Now bypassed, it leads only to Lambton Park.

HEW 331

NZ 285 524

4. Chester-le-Street and Croxdale Viaducts

These two viaducts were built by the North Eastern Railway as part of the improvements to the line between Darlington and Newcastle, one at Chester-le-Street and the other at Croxdale. Both of them have semi-elliptical arches with tapered piers, all in brickwork; the former crosses the town at a height of 84 ft and the latter crosses the River Wear at a height of 74 ft. Both viaducts have eleven spans of 60 ft and a width of 30 ft.

HEW 575

NZ 272 517

HEW 573

NZ 264 376

Both structures were completed under the nominal control of Thomas Elliot Harrison; Chester-le-Street Viaduct was completed in 1868 by Benjamin Carr Lawton and that at Croxdale in 1872 by Thomas Nelson of Carlisle.

Source

TOMLINSON W.W. *The North Eastern Railway*. Longmans Green, London, 1914, 634.

5. Durham Viaduct and Station

HEW 226

NZ 269 426

The viaduct which carries the east coast main line through Durham city was originally built as part of the Bishop Auckland branch of the North Eastern Railway. It comprises eleven semicircular arches of 60 ft span and is 76 ft high. Although the original plans show 3 ft 4 in. span semicircular corbelled arches, the present arrangement is an iron parapet fence fixed to cast iron cantilever brackets, added in 1895.

The structure is of masonry facing with brick soffits to the arches and is built on a curve. The contractor was Richard Cail, responsible for several public works contracts in the region. Similar viaducts were built by him on the same line at Brasside and at Newton Cap; the latter now Grade II listed was converted to road use in 1995. The line included a cutting 80 ft deep at Nevilles Cross; it was opened in 1857, at which time Thomas Elliot Harrison was engineer-in-chief to the railway company.

The stone-slab deck was waterproofed and reinforced with an additional concrete deck by A. Monk & Co. Ltd in 1991 when, as part of the east coast main line electrification, pylons for the overhead wires were installed. At that time it was found that the deck slabs, which were over 130 years old, were still in excellent condition.

HEW 453

NZ 270 428

Immediately north of the viaduct, and built at the same time, stands Durham Station. It did not form part of the main line works until 1870, at which time a new roof was added, unusual in form. A similar roof was built at Selby and there is a smaller one at Hexham. Comprising cast iron Vierendeel-type trusses with a span between columns of 34 ft 6 in. and end cantilevers of 9 ft 10 in., the roof is supported by 8 ft high columns and, with the spandrel supports, provides a clearance of 11 ft 6 in. The trusses are 5 ft deep and spaced at 15 ft centres over 14 bays. Both the original station and the later roof were built while Thomas Prosser was architect to the company.

Sources

TOMLINSON W.W. *The North Eastern Railway*. Longmans Green, London, 1914, 556.

One track timed. *New Civil Engineer*, 23 Mar. 1989, 21–23.

R.W. RENNISON

Durham Viaduct

6. Gilesgate Station, Durham

Gilesgate Station was built as the Durham Branch termi- **HEW 1954**
nus of the Newcastle and Darlington Junction Railway.
It is a simple Georgian classical building, the station **NZ 282 428**
incorporating a two-storey station house at the south-
west corner with the passenger entrance on the west
elevation. It was designed by George T. Andrews and the
contractors were Thompson and Foster. With the line
itself, for which the engineer was Robert Stephenson
assisted by Thomas Elliot Harrison, it was opened in the
presence of George Hudson on 18 June 1844.

The spacings of the columns in the train shed are
unusual, one row comprising six spans of 25 ft and the
other two spans of 36 ft and two of 18 ft. The 10 ft high cast
iron columns support simple cast iron trusses, the spandrels pierced by vertical slits.

The station was used for passengers only until the
completion of the present main line station in 1857, although it continued as a freight terminal until 1966; it
remains in non-rail commercial use.

7. Durham City Bridges

The city of Durham, built on a promontory virtually surrounded by the River Wear and dominated by its cathedral and castle, boasts four bridges of note within its confines, in date spanning from the 12th to the 20th century.

HEW 1867

NZ 276 425

Elvet Bridge was first built circa 1170 but was rebuilt after 1225. It was originally of 14 arches and ten apparently survived until 1978, although only nine can now be seen; the spans range from 23 to 32 ft. The arches are pointed, ribbed and of three orders. Three of the spans were destroyed in the flood of 1771 and the bridge was widened to 30 ft on its upstream side in 1804–05; the widened section has a plain soffit.

HEW 1868

NZ 272 425

Framwellgate Bridge was first built circa 1128 but was rebuilt following a flood in 1401. It has three arches, one hidden by buildings, and those visible are of 87 ft and 82 ft 6 in. span; each is of three orders, originally with five ribs. It was widened in 1856 to give a total width of 27 ft 10 in., the widening incorporating two further ribs.

Framwellgate
Bridge, Durham

Prebends' Bridge was built between 1772 and 1778 to replace an earlier structure destroyed in the 1771 flood,

R.W. RENNISON

which was responsible for so much damage to bridges on both Tyne and Wear. The bridge comprises three semi-circular masonry spans, each of them some 67 ft, with voussoirs and the lower parts of the piers rusticated. Its parapets are part balustraded on a corbel and its height above the river is 40 ft, with a width between parapets of 18 ft 6 in.; refuges are located at each pier. The cathedral's Dean and Chapter were responsible for construction.[1] It is possible that advice was sought from John Wooler, but the bridge was built under the direction of George Nicholson, architect to the cathedral, and John Rennie, commenting on it in 1784, thought it 'a very decent piece of architecture'.[2]

HEW 1966

NZ 271 418

The last of the bridges to be noted is the Kingsgate Bridge and it is fitting that it should have been designed by an engineer born in Newcastle in 1895, (Sir) Ove Arup. This footbridge was built to facilitate access between the new Durham colleges and the older University buildings, and the bridge is notable for the fact that it was constructed in two halves, parallel to the river, the halves being then rotated through $90°$ to form the 350 ft long bridge. The deck is 9 ft wide at a height of 56 ft above the river, and the bridge has been described as a 'thin, taut,

HEW 178

NZ 276 423

Kingsgate Bridge, Durham

R.W. RENNISON

white band stretching horizontally across the valley, resting on a pair of slender tapered fingers in a V-shape rising from each side of the river'.[3] It was built by Holst & Co. Ltd and was completed in 1963.

Sources

1. *Chapter Acts, 1729–1777*. Dean and Chapter (Priors Kitchen), DCD, Durham.

2. MATKIN R.B. (ed.) *John Rennie's diary of a journey through Northern England, 1784*, East Kent Maritime Trust, Ramsgate, 1988, 33.

3. An elegant footbridge at Durham. *Concrete Quarterly*, **60**, Jan.–Mar. 1964, 17–20.

8. Bridge near Escomb, Bishop Auckland

HEW 307

NZ 191 297

The lenticular girder is a type in which the upper member is in compression and the lower in tension, the curvature of the members accounting for the type name. With compressive and tensile forces cancelling each other, the girder imparts only vertical forces to the abutments and piers. The Royal Albert Bridge at Saltash has this form, as has the Gaunless Bridge, and there is also a multi-span example at Roxburgh.

The Bishop Auckland bridge, carrying a farm road over the former Bishop Auckland and Weardale Railway, is intermediate in size, having a clear skew span of 86 ft 3 in. with the two trusses spaced at 11 ft centres. It has a timber deck on timber cross joists at 2 ft 4 in. centres; every 14 ft the cross joist is of iron. The main top member is H-section cast iron and the bottom is wrought iron flat link chain. There are twelve panels incorporating eleven verticals of round bar with diagonal flats alternately rising and falling. The lower bottom member is of square bar coupled to the chain by cast clamps which carry the cross tie-rods, and there are horizontal and vertical cross-bracings of wrought iron flats. The bridge was built in 1842 by the Shildon Works Company in conjunction with John Storey of Darlington.

Source

Information held by Railtrack plc, York.

9. Tunstall Reservoir

The Act which sanctioned the incorporation of the Weardale and Shildon District Waterworks Company also enabled a reservoir to be formed on the Waskerley Beck, near Wolsingham. To design and supervise the work, Thomas Hawksley was appointed Engineer and, under his control, construction was undertaken by direct labour between 1873 and 1879.

HEW 2004

NZ 065 407

The dam holds 520 million gallons of water and comprises an earth embankment 1020 ft long with a puddle clay core and cut-off. The embankment reaches a maximum height of 82 ft above foundation level and the 7 ft diameter draw-off tunnel lies in the hillside at one end of it. Releases of water are controlled by duplicate valves, the upstream one acting as a guard valve and normally left in the open position; the downstream valve acts as the control.

Originally, the cut-off trench in the hillside was filled with puddle clay, but when the reservoir was partially filled it was found to leak. The cut-off was extended, partly by brickwork and partly by concrete, but still leakage continued and Hawksley resorted to the use of grouting, pouring cement grout into a series of borings made along the line of the trench. Tunstall shares with Hawksley's Cowm Reservoir the distinction of having been the earliest earth embankment dam on which grouting techniques were used.

In 1902 the Weardale company amalgamated with the neighbouring Consett Waterworks Company to become the Weardale and Consett Water Company but it, in turn, became the principal constituent of the Durham County Water Board, formed in 1920 and later involved in joint supply schemes with the Sunderland and South Shields Water Company; together the undertakings were involved in the construction of reservoirs at Burnhope and Derwent.

Sources

ASKWITH R. Description of the Weardale and Consett Water-Works. *Trans. Assoc. Water Engrs*, 1909, **14**, 59–64.

BINNIE G. M. *Early dam builders in Britain*. Thomas Telford, London, 1987, 142–143.

10. Seaham Harbour

The 3rd Marquess of Londonderry served with Wellington in the Peninsular campaign of 1809–12 and was later
British Ambassador in Vienna. He acquired the Seaham
Estate in 1821 and, from that time, the mining of coal there
was greatly extended. Coal from the Pittington and Rain-
ton collieries, the property of Londonderry's wife's family, was first shipped from Sunderland, but Londonderry
proposed that a new port should be formed at Seaham,
an idea first put forward by William Chapman for the
former owner of the estate, Sir Ralph Millbanke.

HEW 758

NZ 43 49

After seeking advice from Thomas Telford and (Sir)
John Rennie, plans for the new harbour were prepared
by Chapman and for a new town by John Dobson. An Act
of Parliament was obtained and work began in 1828,
undertaken by direct labour under the control of Chapman and John Buddle, Londonderry's viewer. The construction of both the harbour and its associated railway
was completed in 1831 and, some four years later, the
port was extended by the completion of the South Dock.

Such was the expansion of coal production that the
North Dock was provided with additional coal drops in
1845, but when further expansion was considered it was
decided, instead, to build a railway to Sunderland so that
Seaham Harbour.   coal could be shipped from the Hudson dock there,

Opened in 1850. Following the death of Londonderry in 1854, consideration was again given to extending the harbour, but it was considered more appropriate that additional colliery output should be shipped at Sunderland.

In 1898 the Londonderry port and coal interests were separated, the former becoming the Seaham Harbour Dock Company. To enable the port to compete with others in the region, and with additional capital available, the services of Henry Hay Wake and Patrick Walter Meik were sought. They proposed that a major enlargement of the port be put in hand, and a contract was awarded to S. Pearson & Son Ltd for the construction of two concrete masonry piers, 1383 and 878 ft long, together with a 10 acre dock, its gate 65 ft wide with a depth of 27 ft 6 in. Work began in 1899 and was completed in 1905.

Sources

STURGESS R.W. *An aristocrat in business*. Durham County Local History Society, Durham, 1975.

GASK P.T. The construction of Seaham Harbour dock-works. *Min. Proc. Instn Civ. Engrs*, 1905, **165**, 252–261.

11. Stockton and Darlington Railway

Many claims have been made as to the importance in history of this railway. Although it employed locomotive haulage and carried passengers, its main significance in the North East was that it was built under Act of Parliament—although in this the Middleton Colliery Railway, and others, preceded it—and so was seen as a threat by the coal owners in the region, who were operating waggonways under wayleave agreements. The fact that such agreements resulted in high operating costs led competitors to adopt similar measures.

The Stockton and Darlington Railway was the first major work of George Stephenson and, running via Darlington, was built to carry mineral traffic from Witton Park, to the west of Bishop Auckland, to the River Tees at Stockton. Following an earlier proposal for a canal, an Act for the railway was finally passed in 1821 and the line opened in 1825. Initially it was operated eastwards from Shildon using both locomotives and horses; at its western

HEW 85

NZ 167 294 to 449 183

83

end, stationary engines were installed at the Brusselton and Etherley inclines. Branches were later added at Black Boy and Haggerleazes and in 1830 the system was extended to Middlesbrough.

The permanent way comprised a mixture of cast iron and malleable iron fish-bellied rails supported on stone sleepers and the track, at first only a single line with passing places, was duplicated in 1831. The railway included three bridges of interest, one at the western end of the Haggerleazes branch, one crossing the River Gaunless at West Auckland and another over the River Skerne in Darlington.

HEW 514

NZ 117 256

The bridge at Haggerleazes consists of a single masonry segmental skew arch, a bridge type first used by William Chapman on the Kildare Canal in Ireland in 1787. At Haggerleazes, the angle between the face of the bridge and the face of the abutment is 27° and on its face its span is 42 ft, but its skew reduces this to a true 18 ft; the rise is 7 ft. With a total length of some 85 ft, the width of the bridge is 12 ft. The line was laid out by Robert Stephenson, but this structure has been attributed to Thomas Storey. The piling and foundations were completed by Thomas Worth and John Batey and the arch and parapets were built by James Wilson of Pontefract in 1830.

HEW 190

NZ 186 266

Of the Gaunless Bridge near West Auckland, only the abutments remain. Its iron superstructure, designed by George or Robert Stephenson, was fabricated by John and Isaac Burrell of Newcastle and is now at York, housed in the National Railway Museum there.

HEW 151

NZ 292 156

The Skerne Bridge at Darlington still remains in use. It is of masonry construction, having a central arch of 39 ft 6 in. span with flanking round-headed arches of 8 ft span separated from it by 8 ft wide piers. It was designed by Ignatius Bonomi, a Durham architect, and was built by Francis Peacock of Yarm.

Sources

TOMLINSON W.W. *The North Eastern Railway*. Longmans Green, London, 1914.

STOREY T. Description of the oblique bridge over the River Gaunless on the Hagger Leazes branch railway, Durham. *Min. Proc. Instn Civ. Engrs*, 1845, **4**, 59–61.

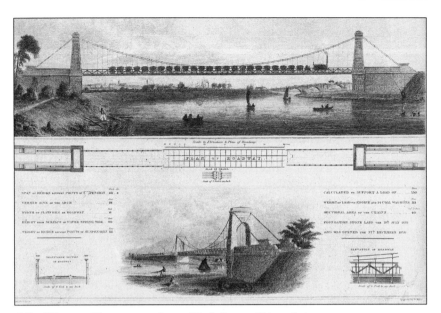

12. Tees Suspension Bridge, Stockton

Tees Suspension Bridge, 1830

Between Stockton and Thornaby the former Stockton and Darlington Railway crosses the River Tees by means of a steel girder bridge, the fourth on this site. The first was the suspension bridge built in 1830 to extend the railway eastwards to what was to become the town of Middlesbrough, then a community of only some 40 inhabitants.

Few bridges have been so significant as this one. Demographically it presaged the establishment of the town of Middlesbrough and technically it proved the impracticability of the use of medium-span suspension bridges for rail traffic. It was 412 ft long with a main span of 281 ft. The deck, 16 ft wide, was suspended from twelve chains and gave a clearance above river level of 20 ft. It was designed by Captain (Sir) Samuel Brown, RN, who was at that time the leading exponent in Britain of this form of construction for road traffic. In spite of Brown's expertise the bridge proved incapable of carrying locomotive traffic without undue movement and, on test with an 18 ton load, the measured deflection proved to be 9¼ in.; later, a load of 66 tons damaged the towers.

To permit traffic to continue using the bridge it was propped and, in 1841, site investigations were made with

HEW 717

NZ 447 179

a view to replacing it. This was done under John Harris and the contractors, Grahamsley and Read, erected a composite girder bridge, designed by Robert Stephenson and similar to that which crossed the River Dee at Chester. Following the collapse of the Dee bridge in 1847, that over the Tees had props inserted and, in this state, it carried traffic until 1881 when a wrought iron bridge was built, using iron cylinders as intermediate piers. In 1906 this structure too was altered and partly superseded by a steel structure, founded on the piled piers of the bridge built in 1841.

Source

McNab C. The river bridges on the Middlesbrough branch of the Stockton and Darlington Railway. *The Cleveland Industrial Archaeologist*, 1979, **11**, 1–6.

13. Middlesbrough Dock

When the Stockton and Darlington Railway was first opened in 1825 coal was shipped at the quay in Stockton itself, immediately downstream of the bridge. It soon became apparent that the river between Stockton and the sea was not adequate for shipping, in spite of the fact that the Tees Navigation Company had formed the cuts at Mandale and Portrack to improve navigation. As a result, the Middlesbrough Owners—in effect, the owners of the town—put in hand the construction of a dock which would both facilitate the shipment of coal and avoid the need for ships to use the still tortuous channel of the Tees.

HEW 1955

NZ 505 207

The engineer for the design and construction of the dock was (Sir) William Cubitt and, with George Turnbull as resident engineer, the dock was completed and brought into service in 1842. It provided a water surface of 9 acres but, with an entrance only 30 ft wide approached by a relatively narrow channel from the river, was soon found to be inadequate.

By this time the dock had come to be fully owned by the Stockton and Darlington Railway, which had previously leased it, and in 1863 it came to form part of the North Eastern Railway. Under Thomas Elliot Harrison, two extensions were made and were completed in 1874 and 1889; the area of the dock was increased to 15¼ acres and the entrance width to 55 ft. Contractors for the first enlargement were Hodgson and Ridley and for the second Sir John Jackson.

The dock's final extension began in 1898, the engineer for the work being Sir John Wolfe Barry. Under him, it was extended to 26 acres and deepened, while the entrance was enlarged to a width of 80 ft with a depth of 33 ft. The contractors were John Scott, of Darlington, with entrance gates provided by Robert Stephenson & Co. and the swing bridge at the entrance supplied by Armstrong Whitworth & Co.

Source

RENNISON R.W. The development of the River Tees, 1808–1914. *Trans. Newcomen Soc.*, 1993–94, **65**, 21–45.

14. River Tees Breakwaters

The earliest of the improvements to the River Tees took place under the Tees Navigation Company, formed in 1808 with the object of eliminating a large meander in the river downstream of Stockton. This work, the Mandale Cut, was carried out under the direction of William Chapman and the formation of a 600 ft long channel reduced the river's length by some 2¼ miles. In 1831 a further cut at Portrack was formed under Henry Habberley Price, but it was not until the Tees Conservancy Commission was established in 1852 that major works were undertaken to improve the river further.

The formation of the Commission was largely a result of the power of the Stockton and Darlington Railway, which promoted two Bills in Parliament, one for the river's improvement and the other for the building of a new harbour at Redcar. Neither came to fruition, but they did result in the formation of a representative body to govern the river, as had already occurred on the Tyne. Advice on improvement was sought from William Bald and plans were prepared for the formation of training walls, for the reclamation of land—unique in the region—and for the construction of breakwaters to protect the river's mouth.

HEW 2005

NZ 55 28

Under the direction of John James Fowler, the works proposed by Bald were put in hand. Unlike the Tyne piers, built contemporaneously in masonry, those at the mouth of the Tees were of ironworks slag. Although the claim that this was the first use of this material was disputed, it is true to say that never before had it been used on such a large scale.

The establishment of the iron industry had led to growing quantities of furnace waste becoming available and difficult to dispose of. River improvement works, and especially the breakwaters, provided an ideal opportunity for its disposal and negotiations led to its being made available in 2–3 ton blocks. The construction of the South Gare breakwater was inaugurated in November 1863, at which time also parliamentary powers were obtained for the formation of a similar structure on the north side of the river's mouth. In cross-section, the breakwater varied but generally it comprised slag blocks, cast for the purpose, faced on the seaward side with a mass concrete wall. The extremity of the breakwater was protected by 30–40 ton concrete blocks placed in a random manner. The South Gare breakwater was completed in 1888 and between 1882 and 1892 the North Gare breakwater, similar in form, was built by George Dawson.

Some 5 million tons of slag were used for the building of the south breakwater and the northern one took some 750 000 tons. River dredging continued and, by 1914, approximately 22 million tons of material had been removed from the channel, more than 2 million tons in 1888 alone. Land reclamation totalled 2000 acres, this work having entailed the building of 14 miles of embankment. The greater part of the work had been carried out under Fowler, but his death in 1888 had brought in George James Clarke as engineer.

Source

FOWLER J. River Tees improvements. *Min. Proc. Instn Civ. Engrs*, 1886–87, **90**, 344–357.

15. Hartlepool Docks

HEW 664

NZ 51 33

The present port of Hartlepool originated as two separate undertakings. The Hartlepool Dock and Railway Company was established in 1832 to provide a new dock with a railway from mines lying to the north-west of the port;

its promoters were mainly colliery owners. The basin at Hartlepool was opened in 1835 and the shipping of coal then began; it was not until 1840 that the adjoining 19 acre Victoria Dock was completed. The engineer for the dock and railway was, at first, James Milne, but after some dispute his position concerning the dock was taken by James Brown, acting under Sir John Rennie. The engineer for the railway was Stephen Robinson, George Stephenson having been initially appointed.

The docks at West Hartlepool owe their existence to the extension to the port of the Clarence Railway. Initially, it was intended that coal should be diverted from the Stockton and Darlington Railway and shipped at the docks already established. Co-operation soon proved difficult and, as a result, the Hartlepool West Harbour and Dock Company was formed, combining with the Stockton and Hartlepool Railway under the control of Ralph Ward Jackson. The first of the new docks, the 8 acre Coal Dock, was opened in 1847. Expansion led to the opening of the 14 acre Jackson Dock in 1852 and the 10 acre Swainson Dock in 1856.

By this time new breakwaters had been completed to protect the docks, but who designed them is unclear. James Simpson was responsible for the first plans but the

Hartlepool Docks

UNIVERSITY OF NEWCASTLE/SOCIETY OF ANTIQUITIES

piers were remodelled after 1849 by Thomas Casebourne. However, Jackson's involvement cannot be ruled out, his obituary recording that 'a series of inner piers designed by Mr. Jackson... formed a unique system of "wave traps" in the harbour'.[1] The first section of the work was carried out by Thomas Hutchinson of Ferryhill.

The formation of the North Eastern Railway led to the original docks becoming part of it in 1857, and in 1865 the later docks came under its control too. It was not until 1874 that any move was made to enlarge the port further, but three additional docks, of 3, 13 and 12½ acres were then added, joining together the two systems. Under Thomas Elliot Harrison, William George Laws was responsible for at least part of the work. Begun in 1875 with Charles Augustus Harrison directing work, the dock complex was opened in July 1880, having been built by (Sir) Walter Scott.[2]

Sources

1. Memoirs, *Min. Proc. Instn Civ. Engrs*, 1881, **63**, 328–332.

2. RENNISON R.W. The development of the ports of the Durham coalfield, 1825–1865. *Symposium on the history of technology, science and society, 1750–1914.* University of Ulster, Sept. 1989.

16. Middlesbrough Transporter Bridge

Middlesbrough expanded from a population of 154 in 1831 to 91 302 in 1901 and, to improve communications to the north, an Act of Parliament was obtained in 1907 for the construction of a bridge, conditional upon river navigation not being affected.

In the 1870s Charles Smith, manager of Hartlepool Ironworks, had put forward the idea of a bridge consisting of a fixed high-level girder with a suspended car to carry passengers. His ideas had subsequently been developed by Ferdinand Arnodin whose first bridge of this type, at Bilbao, Spain, was opened in 1893, followed six years later by one at Rouen, France.

HEW 10

NZ 501 213

At Middlesbrough, the design comprises a travelling car, tested to a load of 80 tons, suspended by wires from a carriage running along the girders, the car carrying up to 600 persons or an equivalent load of vehicles across the

river in 2½ minutes. The steel truss carrying the carriage has a span of 565 ft between the towers and gives a clearance above high water of 160 ft. Cantilever end spans each 140 ft long balance the main spans and are anchored to the ground by steel cables.

Middlesbrough Transporter Bridge

The bridge was opened by Prince Arthur of Connaught in October 1911, having been designed by Cleveland Bridge and Engineering Ltd. The contractors were Sir William Arrol & Co. Ltd and Cleveland Bridge & Engineering Ltd. Similar bridges were erected at Runcorn, Warrington and Newport, Gwent; the first of these has been demolished.

Sources

FORBES N.N. *Transporter bridges.* Light Railway Transport League, no date, 9, 10.

The Transporter Bridge over the River Tees. *Engineer*, 1911, **112**, 336–337.

17. Newport Lift Bridge, Middlesbrough

The Lift Bridge crosses the River Tees at Newport and was opened by the Duke and Duchess of York in February 1934; it was designed by Mott, Hay and Anderson and

HEW 470

NZ 478 199

91

Newport Lift
Bridge

CLEVELAND CITY COUNCIL

was built by Dorman Long & Co. Ltd. So that shipping could pass upstream, the solution adopted was to provide a bridge with a lifting section, in its raised position providing the requisite clearance. At Newport, the headroom of 21 ft when lowered is increased to 120 ft when raised; navigation width is 250 ft. The lifting operation is by means of ropes passing through sheaves at the corner towers, each 182 ft high, and the lifting or lowering operation is completed in approximately 1½ minutes. Operation is by means of two 325 h.p. motors and the weight of the lifting section is 1530 tons.

The bridge structure is carried on cast iron cylinders filled with concrete and sunk to a depth of 86 ft below high water level. Some 28 000 tons of concrete were used during construction, and the weight of steel in the bridge and its approach spans is 8000 tons. Because of the cessation of shipping passing upstream to Stockton and as a result of high maintenance and operating costs, the lifting span was secured in its lowered position in 1990; it continues to carry vehicular traffic.

HEW 2006

NZ 475 201

On the north bank of the Tees and forming one of the approach roads to the Lift Bridge is what is reputedly the earliest all-welded bridge in Britain; forming part of the Lift Bridge contract, it too was opened in 1934. The Welded Bridge comprises five spans of 28, 48, 64, 48 and 28 ft respectively, the end spans being, in effect, half spans terminating at road level at the abutments. The continuous longitudinal portal frames, nine in number, are carried on 3 ft ll in. diameter cylinders, extending to a depth of 70 ft and braced at their upper ends by reinforced concrete ground beams. The 55 ft wide bridge crosses the railway at a slight skew. The lower ends of the portal columns, which taper from 3 ft 2 in. at the top to 18 in. at the bottom, rest on rocker bearings, in turn supported by the piles.

Sources

HAMILTON J.A.K. and GRAVES J.T. Tees (Newport) Bridge, Middlesbrough. *Min. Proc. Instn Civ. Engrs*, 1935, **240**, 567–617.

HALDANE W.P. Billingham Branch Bridge. *Min. Proc. Instn Civ. Engrs*, 1935, **240**, 537–566.

18. Victoria Bridge, Stockton

In 1881 Stockton Corporation obtained an Act of Parliament for the replacement of the deteriorating masonry multi-arch bridge completed in 1771. The construction of this bridge had, in part, led to the decline of Yarm as a port, a result of the bridge's relatively small arches.

The replacement bridge was designed by Harrison Hayter and Charles Neate and construction began in 1882. Foundations for abutments and piers comprised 14 ft diameter cylinders, some 40 ft deep, rows of five cylinders being used at both piers and abutments. As a result of the ground conditions encountered during construction, it was found necessary to use compressed air working for the sinking of the cylinders.

HEW 559

NZ 449 183

The abutments are masonry-faced and are filled with large stone random rubble. The bridge structure comprises spans of 85, 110 and 85 ft with wrought iron two-pinned plate girders; there are eight ribs per arch, the girders being 4 ft deep at the bearings and 3 ft at the centre. The deck is carried on buckled plates supported by secondary beams which, in turn, are carried by the main arch ribs. The parapets and the bridge spandrels comprise ornamental castings. Built by Whitaker Bros of Leeds, the bridge was opened in June 1887.

Source

NEATE C. Memoir of the Victoria Bridge, Stockton-on-Tees. *Min. Proc. Instn Civ. Engrs*, 1891–92, **109**, 304–311.

19. Yarm Bridge

HEW 558

NZ 418 131

The masonry bridge which crosses the River Tees at Yarm dates from circa 1400, but replaced an earlier bridge there, perhaps dating from the 13th century. By the end of the 18th century it came to be considered inadequate, largely because of its width of 12 ft, and an iron bridge with a span of 180 ft and width of 27 ft was built.

The iron bridge was the work of Thomas Wilson, earlier involved with Rowland Burdon at Sunderland, and construction began in 1803; the arches were erected and the bridge completed by September 1805. On 16 September 1805, success to the bridge was toasted by the ex-Mayor of Stockton—while actually standing on the bridge—but, as Wardell comments, on 13 January 1806 'the unlucky bridge, which had cost so much money and temper, fell into the river with a tremendous crash... owing to the collapse of the south abutment'.

Following this failure, the old masonry bridge, with its five spans of up to 50 ft, was widened on its downstream side to provide a width of 35 ft.

Sources

WARDELL J.W. *A history of Yarm*. Wardell, Sunderland. 1957, 121–122.

CHETTOE C.S. and HENDERSON W. Masonry arch bridges. *Proc. Instn Civ. Engrs*, 1977, 7, 723–774.

20. Yarm Viaduct

The Leeds and Thirsk Railway was formed in 1845 to provide communication from Leeds to the north. The line to Thirsk was completed in 1848 and, following an agreement made with Ralph Ward Jackson, the railway—from 1851 renamed the Leeds Northern—was extended to Stockton, so reaching the Durham coalfield and the port of Hartlepool.

HEW 581

NZ 418 125 to 417 133

In addition to the viaduct at Knaresborough, another was built to cross the Tees at Yarm. With a total length of almost half a mile, it comprises 41 brick land arches of 40 ft span and two masonry skew river arches of 67 ft, rising to 65 ft above the river. The initial design, by Thomas Grainger, was for a single arch of 125 ft span. It was opened on 15 May 1852, the contractors having been Trowsdale, Jackson and Garbutt.

Source

TOMLINSON W.W. *The North Eastern Railway.* Longmans Green, London, 1914, 513.

21. Blackwell Bridge, Darlington

With semi-elliptical spans of 68, 78 and 68 ft, the bridge was designed by John Green, his first masonry bridge, and was opened in 1832. It carries the former Great North Road over the River Tees and is built of sandstone from Gatherley Moor; it was widened most sympathetically in 1961. Like Telford's bridge at Morpeth, the arches incorporate *cornes-de-vache*, but in a less pronounced form.

HEW 533

NZ 270 126

Source

HAGGER H. The Bridges of John Green. *Northern Architect*, 1976, **8**, 25–31.

22. Darlington North Road Station

The present North Road station is not the earliest on this site but was built in 1842 by the Stockton and Darlington

Darlington North Road Station

NORTH ROAD STATION MUSEUM, DARLINGTON

HEW 288

NZ 289 157

Railway and has been altered since then. The station, now a museum, comprises a single-storey range of offices some 400 ft in length with a central two-storey bay, fronted by a canopy which is supported by seven cast iron columns. Behind it is the train shed, which comprises timber trusses of 55 ft span. Extended in 1873, it has since been reduced to its original size.

Internally, the station features an attractive cast iron spiral staircase and houses amongst its exhibits the two locomotives, *Locomotion No. 1* and *Derwent*, which for many years were a feature of the present main-line station in the town.

Source

PEVSNER N. and WILLIAMSON E. *The buildings of England: County Durham.* Penguin, London, 1990, 149.

23. Darlington Bank Top Station

HEW 439

NZ 294 141

Darlington station is based upon an island platform served by a central subway from the west and a vehicular access at the north end. Station buildings are located on the island spine and there are bay lines at each end of the station. The overall roof is more than 1000 ft long with three spans of wrought iron arched ribs varying from 62 ft to 66 ft at 19 ft to 27 ft centres, supported on cast iron columns and arcades; in all there are 47 bays. Cast iron plates used as facings to the structural members incorporate the arms of the North Eastern Railway and the places served by it. Lattice purlins at 4 ft 7 in. centres are covered with boarding and slates in the lower parts of the arch and by roof glazing above.

The station buildings are of brick with sandstone dressings and there is a large *porte-cochère* with a tower at the west entrance. The station was designed by William Bell and, with James Thompson as contractor, was completed in 1887.

Source

PEVSNER N. and WILLIAMSON E. *The buildings of England: County Durham.* Penguin, London, 1990, 149–150.

24. Darlington Pumping Station

The Darlington Gas and Water Company was formed by the Pease family in 1849 and some five years later the works were taken over, partly by what was to become the Darlington Corporation Water Department and partly by the Stockton, Middlesbrough and Yarm Water Company, later the Tees Valley Water Board.

A pumping station had been built at Darlington in 1849 to abstract water from the River Tees and in 1903 these works were extended by the Corporation and a further pumping station built. The pump house, designed by T.& C. Hawksley, houses a beam engine built by Teesdale Brothers of Darlington, believed to be the last of this type of engine installed in a British waterworks.

HEW 534

NZ 258 139

The engine works at a steam pressure of 100 pounds per square inch, the cylinders of 18 in. and 29 in. diameter and the stroke of 5 ft 3 in. being such as to produce 140 h.p. The pumps were capable of raising 1800 gallons per minute to a head of 125 ft.

In 1913 a Hornsby gas engine of 200 h.p. was installed in a nearby building, its cylinder being $18\frac{1}{4}$ in. diameter with a stroke of 24 in. Gas was generated on site and the engine powers Hathorn Davey pumps of duty similar to the beam engine. The station is no longer in service but is now in the ownership of Northumbrian Water plc and is operated periodically.

Source

Information held by Northumbrian Water plc.

25. Whorlton Bridge

On 13 October 1829, the Whorlton bridge, then under construction, was destroyed by a flood on the River Tees and John Green, of Newcastle, was called upon to prepare designs for its replacement. At this time the Scotswood suspension bridge—demolished in 1967—was being built to his designs and it was this form of construction which he chose for use at Whorlton.

The bridge spans 183 ft and the suspension cables, stretching from individual masonry pillars, comprise links made up from flat wrought iron bars 9 ft 7 in. long,

HEW 356

NZ 106 145

Whorlton Bridge · 3 in. deep and 1 in. wide; the bridge is supported by its original chains. Cross-bracing is of wrought iron and the bridge deck is of timber; the 18 ft wide deck is suspended from the cables at 4 ft 6 in. intervals.

Begun in 1830, the bridge was opened in July 1831. Damaged by gales in 1976, it is now subject to a weight restriction of three tons.

Source

HAGGER H. The bridges of John Green. *Northern Architect,* 1976, **8,** 25–31.

26. Wynch Bridge

HEW 814

NY 904 279

In 1821 the River Tees was credited with the first permanent suspension bridge in Europe, built in 1741 some two miles upstream of Middleton-in-Teesdale.[1] The Wynch Bridge was said to have had a single span of some 70 ft with a width of 2 ft and was restrained by further chains connecting the deck to the rock face below it. It would seem to have been used principally by miners and, with a handrail only on one side, those crossing it experienced a 'tremulous motion of the chain...on an agitated, restless gangway to which few strangers dare trust themselves'.[2]

The bridge was described by Thomas Sopwith in 1833,

however, as having a span of marginally less than 60 ft, with the chain links 6 in. by 1¾ in., formed of bar iron ½ in. by ⅜ in. On the chains were placed wooden cross-rails at 3 ft 6 in. spacings and, on them, longitudinal planking was laid, forming a deck 1 ft 9 in. wide; hand-rails were provided on each side.[3]

The bridge collapsed in 1802 or 1820—both dates have been given—following which it was replaced by another suspension bridge of sturdier design, perhaps that described by Sopwith. This in turn was replaced by the present structure early in the 20th century.

Sources

1. STEVENSON R. Description of bridges of suspension. *Edinburgh Philosophical Journal*, 1821.

2. HUTCHINSON W. *The history and antiquities of the County Palatine of Durham*. Carlisle, 1794, 3, 179–280.

3. SOPWITH T. *An account of the mining district of Alston Moor, Weardale and Teesdale*. W. Davidson, Alnwick, 1833, 153–155.

27. Hury and Blackton Reservoirs

The group of impounding reservoirs on the headwaters of the River Tees was built, from 1884 onwards, to supply the unprecedented increase in population of the towns on Teesside. The earliest supplies there had been provided by the Stockton, Middlesbrough and Yarm Water Company, formed in 1851, which became the Stockton and Middlesbrough Water Board in 1876, the Tees Valley Water Board in 1899 and the Tees Valley and Cleveland Water Board in 1956.

HEW 2007

NY 967 196 and NY 948 187

At the time of the 1876 reorganization, the works had comprised pumping stations and filters at Broken Scar, on the Tees near Darlington, but to augment supplies the Board sought powers for the building of reservoirs on the streams feeding the Tees in its upper reaches. Hury Reservoir was designed by James Mansergh and work was undertaken by (Sir) Walter Scott & Co. of Newcastle. The earth embankment is approximately 1100 ft long with a maximum height above the impounded River Balder of 90 ft. A concrete cut-off was provided to render water-tight the underlying strata—boulder clay overlying shales and sandstone—and above it the puddle clay core

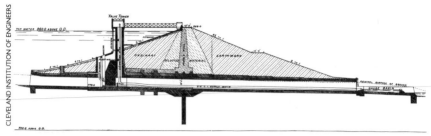

CLEVELAND INSTITUTION OF ENGINEERS

Hury Reservoir:
section through
embankment

was formed, supported by the earth embankment; the core is 22 ft wide at its base, tapering to 6 ft at the dam's crest. Water is taken from the 859 million gallon capacity reservoir by means of a 36 in. diameter outlet main, in turn fed from draw-off valves at three levels; the main runs through a brick-lined tunnel built into the embankment. Such were the problems encountered that the final cost of £218 335 was more than double the original tender price. The reservoir became operational in 1892.

While construction was in progress, rain and river gaugings showed that this reservoir alone would not be sufficient to meet demand, and another, Blackton, immediately upstream and on similar strata, was put in hand by the same contractor. With a capacity of 460 million gallons, an embankment length of some 725 ft and a height of 71 ft, it was begun in 1889 and completed in 1896. Whereas Hury originally had a spillway overflow partially elliptical in plan, that at Blackton took the form of a bell-mouth 45 ft in diameter with a tunnel leading to a smaller reservoir between the two larger ones. The tunnel is lined with cast iron plates and has a diameter of 13 ft 6 in. Unlike Hury, Blackton has no separate and direct outlet; water from it is fed into the lower reservoir.

An increasing demand for water led to the construction of Grassholme Reservoir (NY 947 229), begun by John Scott, of Cotherstone, in 1900. As a result of poor ground conditions it was not completed until 1914 and its final cost of £534 150 was almost three times the tender price. Water is taken from it by means of a tunnel to Hury and the output of all three reservoirs was treated by filters at Lartington, built between 1896 and 1901.

Source

MACAULAY F.W. *The gravitation works of the Stockton and Middlesbrough Water Board*. Cleveland Institute of Engineers, Session 1896–97, 10–40.

28. Cow Green Reservoir

Increasing industrialization on Teesside, principally the establishment at Billingham of the works of Imperial Chemical Industries in 1920, led to further demands for water and Selset Reservoir, above Grassholme, was completed in 1960, one of the last uses in Britain of a puddle clay core. Balderhead Reservoir, above Blackton, was brought into service in 1965. The last of the reservoirs to be constructed in this area was Cow Green, located immediately upstream of Cauldron Snout; it does not have a pipeline leading from it but was built for the purpose of regulating the flow of the River Tees.

HEW 2008

NY 814 289

The underlying strata comprise an outcrop of the Whin Sill on the Durham side of the valley and boulder clay on the Cumbria side and, as a result, it was found economical to form a length of dam in concrete, based on rock, and to complete it by means of an earth embankment. The total length of the dam is 1875 ft and the length of the concrete section is 1080 ft.

The concrete section of the dam rises to a height of 82 ft above foundation level and joints are provided at 46 ft intervals, the individual sections made watertight by means of copper strips; an inspection gallery runs through it. Part of the concrete section forms the reservoir's overflow, its length 225 ft. The earth embankment, without a cut-off, incorporates a rolled boulder clay core and the fill supporting it is predominantly gravel, topped with clay; the side slopes are 1 in 3½.

Cow Green Reservoir contains water to a maximum depth of 75 ft and its topwater level of 1603 ft makes it one of the highest reservoirs in Britain. Its capacity of 8976 million gallons is similar to the total of all the earlier reservoirs taken together. It was designed by Sandeman, Kennard and Partners and built by the Mitchell Construction Company. The enabling Act was passed in March 1967, work began almost immediately and the reservoir was completed in 1970.

Source

KENNARD M.F. and READER R.A. Cow Green dam and reservoir. *Min. Proc. Instn Civ. Engrs*, 1975, **58**, 147–175.

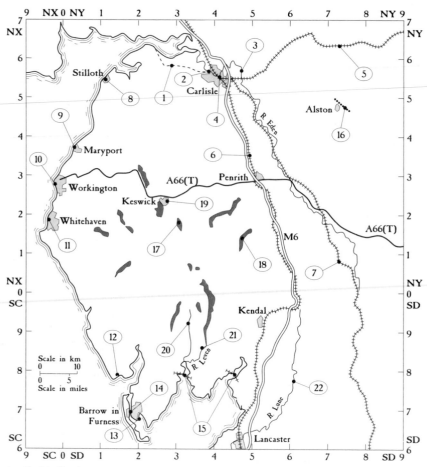

1	Carlisle Canal
2	Shaddon Mill, Carlisle
3	Warwick Bridge, near Carlisle
4	Carlisle Citadel Station
5	Newcastle and Carlisle Railway
6	Lancaster and Carlisle Railway
7	Smardale Viaduct
8	Silloth Docks
9	Maryport Docks
10	Workington Harbour
11	Whitehaven Harbour

12	Hodbarrow Sea Defences
13	Barrow-in-Furness Docks
14	Walney Bridge, Barrow
15	Kent and Leven Viaducts
16	Nent Force Level
17	Thirlmere Reservoir
18	Haweswater Reservoir
19	Station Road Bridge, Keswick
20	Satterthwaite Bridge
21	Newby Bridge
22	Devil's Bridge, Kirkby Lonsdale

4. Cumbria

The present-day county of Cumbria comprises the former counties of Cumberland and Westmorland, together with the Furness district of Lancashire. It is bounded to the west by the Irish Sea and to the east by the north Pennines, the massive Ordovician and Silurian rocks of the central core of the Lake District lying between and forming a barrier little penetrated until the coming of the railways.

In the Pennines are lead deposits, and some coal, centred on Alston, formerly a thriving lead-mining area. To the west, near to the sea and even under it, are deposits of coal, those at Whitehaven having been worked before 1550. It was, however, iron which brought the greatest prosperity to the southern part of the county, the discovery in about 1850 of a major deposit

Joseph Locke (1805–60)

of haematite leading to the rise of Barrow-in-Furness and the establishment of an iron and steel industry in the south-western corner of the county.

Cumbria boasted three canals, although one of them was soon transformed into a railway. One of the first railways was that bringing iron ore for shipment at Barrow, and the rail network was developed with the forming of the west coast main line and the linking by rail of the two major iron-manufacturing areas in the north of England, West Cumbria and

Wetheral Viaduct, Newcastle and Carlisle Railway

Teesside. One of the last major railways in England, and the last of the navvy-built lines, was that between Settle and Carlisle, completed in 1875.

Port development generally was associated with both mineral working and with railways. Whitehaven's existence, however, was of long standing and Defoe referred to it as 'the most eminent Port of England for shipping off Coals, except Newcastle and Sunderland, and even before the last, for they wholly supply the City of Dublin, and all the Towns of Ireland on that Coast'; the development of other coal-exporting ports followed. Barrow grew in response to the iron trade and later it became a major shipbuilding town, a position it still retains in 1996.

The Lake District is notorious for its high rainfall and it is unsurprising that it became a major source of water for Lancashire, especially Manchester. Several of its lakes, some formed by impounding reservoirs, supply water for domestic purposes, and great credit must be given for the inconspicuous way in which this has been achieved.

Source

DEFOE D. *A tour through the whole island of Great Britain*. Peter Davies, London, 1927, **2**, 683 (first published 1724–1727).

1. Carlisle Canal

After earlier proposals for a canal between Carlisle and the Solway, involving both William Chapman and Thomas Telford, another was made by Chapman in 1818. His proposals were incorporated in an Act of Parliament which was passed the following year; construction began almost immediately and the canal was completed in 1823. It was 11½ miles long and included six locks and two basins in its length, together with the terminal basin in Carlisle, the latter being connected later by rail to the Newcastle and Carlisle Railway. Its locks were 74 ft by 17 ft and were capable of passing barges of up to 100 tons. Water was supplied from a reservoir near Kirkandrews and, by pumping, from the River Eden.

HEW 969

NY 391 560 to 241 622

The canal achieved a modest success until the coming of the railways and, indeed, contributed to their adoption by conveying the locomotive *Rocket* on its way from Newcastle by road, canal and sea to Liverpool for the 1829 Rainhill Trials. In 1853–54 it was converted to a railway and the canal drawbridges were replaced by cast iron girder bridges, several of which still remain. The goods shed of the later railway still stands in Carlisle, built upon the former canal basin. As a railway, from 1856 the main line ran to new docks at Silloth and the section between Drumburgh and Port Carlisle became a branch line, worked until 1914 by a horse-drawn passenger coach. The canal warehouse built in 1823 at the Carlisle basin was demolished in 1974, but the coal and lime vaults remain; at Port Carlisle the warehouses have been converted into houses and many of the lock- and bridge-keepers' houses still remain, as well as the sea-lock chamber.

The end of Port Carlisle came in 1868 when one of the longest railway viaducts in Europe was built across the Solway downstream of it, and without an opening span. It was 5790 ft long with 181 piers and designed by (Sir) James Brunlees, who also built the Kent and Leven viaducts. It had five-column braced trestle piers and 30 ft span plate girders. Opened in 1869, the viaduct was severely damaged in 1875–76 and in 1881 partially destroyed by ice; it was repaired and re-opened in 1884, but

HEW 714

NY 206 645 to 211 628

was finally demolished in 1934–35, having been unused since 1921.

Sources

HADFIELD C. and BIDDLE G. *The canals of North West England*. David and Charles, Newton Abbot, 1970, 336–348.

MULLAY A.J. *Rails across the border*. Patrick Stephens Ltd, Wellingborough, 1990, 126–156.

2. Shaddon Mill, Carlisle

HEW 961

NY 395 556

At the time of its completion in 1836 the Shaddon Mill in Carlisle was the largest cotton mill in England. The seven-storey mill building is 225 ft long by 60 ft wide and reached a height of 83 ft, with a chimney towering above

Shaddon Mill, Carlisle

it to a height of 305 ft. The main beams span 18 ft between 6½ in. diameter columns; the beams are spaced at 9 ft 3 in. centres and shallow brick vaulting carries tiled floors with 10 ft 6 in. headroom.

The mill was built for Peter Dixon, at one time employing 8000 people in the area, and its design was by Robert Tattersall of Manchester with the interior cast iron framing and machinery designed by (Sir) William Fairbairn. The contractors were Richard Wright for the chimney and Nixon and Denton for the mill itself.

Source

JONES E. *Industrial architecture in Britain, 1750–1939*. Batsford, London, 1985, 58–59.

3. Warwick Bridge, near Carlisle

Warwick Bridge carries the A69(T) road, running between Carlisle and Newcastle, over the River Eden some four miles east of the former town. It comprises three spans, two of 75 ft each, with a central span of 80 ft, all arches segmental in form; it is 24 ft wide.

The bridge was built at the behest of Peter Dixon, owner of the Shaddon Mill, who later lived in the nearby Holme Eden Hall. Concerned about the dangerous

HEW 2011

NY 469 567

Warwick Bridge

R.W. RENNISON

condition of the old bridge, he obtained the services of Francis Giles, engineer for the bridge works of the Newcastle and Carlisle Railway, to inspect it. Giles concluded that a replacement bridge was needed. It is, perhaps no coincidence that Dixon was a director of the railway company.

A dispute then arose involving William Sanderson, the County Bridgemaster, and Dixon, the outcome being that Giles submitted a lower and more acceptable price for the bridge's replacement than that which he had first submitted. He achieved this by reducing the width of the structure. Eventually, as his estimate had been brought nearer that which had been submitted by Sanderson, work was put in hand by William Smith Denton and John Dobson, of whom the former was later responsible for Wetheral Viaduct and possibly Shaddon Mill. Under the supervision of Giles the bridge was begun in 1833 and completed in 1835.

Source

Cumberland News, 21 Apr. 1989.

4. Carlisle Citadel Station

As one of the principal links in the west coast route to Scotland, Carlisle Citadel Station was originally built to serve the Lancaster and Carlisle and the Caledonian railways and was opened in 1847. The main station buildings were designed by (Sir) William Tite and built by John Stephenson.

HEW 537

NY 402 555

The station buildings are 470 ft long and incorporate a clock tower and a portico on which are displayed the heraldic devices adopted by the two original railway companies. It was at first intended that the arms of the Newcastle and Carlisle and the Maryport and Carlisle railways should also be displayed, as they too were involved in the negotiations for a joint station. Eventually, no fewer than seven railway companies used it.

The opening of the Settle and Carlisle line brought extra traffic into the joint station. Additional tracks, platforms and buildings became necessary and the present station roof, a listed structure, was built between 1873 and 1876 as part of this enlargement scheme. Of iron and

Carlisle Citadel
Station

R.W. RENNISON

glass, the roof initially covered an overall area of 6½ acres and it was carried on 26 deep lattice or double Warren girders at 40 ft centres, each with ten panels, stiffened end posts and a flat bottom tie. The spaces between the girders are filled with balanced cantilevered half-trusses at centres approximating to 12 ft, the roof covering being mainly patent glazing. The effect is of extreme lightness and yet ample strength. Much of the roof, including the Gothic end screens, was removed in 1958. The engineers for the roof's construction were Blythe and Cunningham.

HEW 437

NY 402 555

Source

SANDERS E.M. Notable railway stations and their traffic. Carlisle (Citadel), London Midland and Scottish Railway. *Railway Mag.*, June 1923, **52,** 431–438.

5. Newcastle and Carlisle Railway

It has already been noted in Chapter 1 that work on the construction of the Newcastle and Carlisle Railway began in 1829. Under the direction of Francis Giles, the four principal works at its western end were built: they are the Wetheral and Corby viaducts, the Gelt Bridge and the Cowran cutting.

HEW 962

NZ 245 637 to NY 403 554

The Wetheral Viaduct consists of five semicircular arches, each of 80 ft span, and the railway is carried at a height of 93 ft across the River Eden. Iron cantilevers carry a footbridge on the north face of the viaduct. The

HEW 720

NY 469 546

comparable statistics for the Corby Viaduct (NY 473 548), crossing the Drybeck, are seven arches of 40 ft with a height of 60 ft. Both structures are built in red sandstone with piers 25 ft wide and each has a width between parapets of 22 ft. The contractor was William Denton.

HEW 719

NY 532 573

Some five miles to the east of the Eden crossing is the Gelt Bridge, a skew bridge with three arches, each of approximately 30 ft, carrying the twin tracks at a height of 60 ft above the river; it was built by John McKay.

The Cowran cutting (NY 516 567 to 531 571) was initially intended to have been a tunnel, but a change in design was made necessary as a result of the ground conditions. It extends over a length of almost a mile with a maximum depth of 110 ft and a maximum width of 305 ft. The slopes of the sides are 1 in 1½ and, to reduce width, 14 ft high masonry retaining walls support their lower edges. The total volume of earth removed from the cutting was almost a million cubic yards. The first section of the line, from Carlisle to Greenhead, was opened in July 1836.

Sources

CARMICHAEL J.G. and BLACKMORE J. *Views on the Newcastle and Carlisle Railway*. Currie and Bowman, Newcastle upon Tyne, 1836–38.

TOMLINSON W.W. *The North Eastern Railway*. Longmans Green, London, 1914, 261.

6. Lancaster and Carlisle Railway

HEW 958

SD 472 617 to
NY 402 555

The Lancaster and Carlisle Railway was authorized by Act of Parliament in 1844, by which time the heaviest gradients of 1 in 75 over Shap Summit were considered practicable. The line, now forming part of the west coast main line, runs northwards from Lancaster, bypassing Kendal to the east, but with a branch to it from Oxenholme, before crossing Shap summit at 914 ft and continuing through Penrith. Passing through the Lune Gorge, the railway shares it with the river, the M6 and the A685.

HEW 596

SD 566 957

Of the viaducts on the line, that at Dockwray— also known as Dockers Garth or Fiddlers Gill—carries the line over a tributary of the River Mint at a height of 50 ft. The six segmental arches of 50 ft span comprise brick soffits

with white limestone piers and arch facings. Another viaduct is that crossing the River Lowther some three miles south of Penrith. Its six semicircular spans are of 60 ft with the piers tapering from 13 ft 6 in. at the base to 8 ft at the arch springing.

Lowther Viaduct

HEW 597

NY 525 270

Work on the building of the railway began in July 1844 and was completed in December 1846. Joseph Locke and John Edward Errington were appointed as joint engineers, but because of Locke's other commitments the greater part of the work was undertaken by Errington; the contractor was McKenzie, Stephenson & Co.

Although the line's original viaducts with their tapering piers are very graceful, it is the now disused Lowgill Viaduct on the Ingleton Branch, opened in 1861, after Locke's death, which is the most notable. It not only has restrained decoration which gives it character, but it is larger than those on the main line, having eleven arches of 45 ft span and a height of 88 ft; the contractor was Samuel Buxton.

HEW 721

SD 616 965

Source

REED B. *Crewe to Carlisle*. Ian Allan, London, 1969.

7. Smardale Viaduct

With its length divided between Cumbria and North Yorkshire, the Settle and Carlisle line itself is described in Chapter 5. Among the individual works along its length, including the spectacular Ribblehead Viaduct, is a smaller structure at Smardale, notable as being, at 130 ft, the highest on the Midland Railway. The viaduct is approximately 710 ft long with twelve spans and it is built

HEW 960

NY 732 081

of local grey limestone with parapets and arch quoins of millstone grit. The original intention was to provide a second set of six arches at a lower level between the two larger piers, but this proposal was abandoned and all the piers were built to full height.

The viaduct spanned not only Scandal Beck, but also the South Durham and Lancashire Union Railway, originally part of the Stockton and Darlington Railway's development to connect the Barrow-in-Furness area in the west with Teesside in the east, a line which opened in 1861. The Chief Engineer of the Midland Railway was John Sidney Crossley and, with John S. Storey as resident engineer and Benton and Woodiwiss as contractors, the viaduct was first used in August 1875.

Sources

BAUGHAN R.E. *The Midland Railway north of Leeds*. David and Charles, Newton Abbot, 1987.

MITCHELL W.R. and JOY D. *Settle and Carlisle Railway*. Dalesman Books, Clapham, N. Yorks, 1967.

8. Silloth Docks

From 1823 the city of Carlisle had been connected to the sea by means of a canal, reaching the Solway at Port Carlisle. This mode of transport had not proved as satisfactory as the Carlisle manufacturers would have wished and, as a result, an Act of Parliament was obtained in 1853 for the conversion of the canal to a railway. Its completion, however, did not totally alleviate the problem of ships being called upon to pass through narrow shifting channels unsuitable for large vessels.

To improve matters further, the Carlisle and Silloth Railway and Dock Company was formed by William Marshall MP to construct a railway to Silloth, where there was a deep inshore channel, and build there a pier and wet dock. Designed by John Hartley, the scheme was submitted for parliamentary approval in 1854, when it was refused after bitter opposition, but then resubmitted and finally passed the following year.

The 12 mile railway was completed by Thomas Nelson, a Carlisle contractor, in 1856, but it was a further year before the construction of the dock began. To utilize the

HEW 2012

NY 10 53

railway and help finance dock construction, the company promoted Silloth as a resort, with high-quality buildings erected on a well-planned and serviced street system provided by the company under the control of Liverpool architects, Messrs Hay. Manufacturers were persuaded to build their factories adjacent to the town.

The 4 acre dock was completed in 1859, its designs having been prepared by James Abernethy, who had succeeded Hartley, and the work undertaken by Nelson. Construction took place within a semicircular embankment, water being removed from the construction area by pumping from wells. A 1000 ft long timber pier projected in front of the dock, alongside a 100 ft wide dredged channel; the water depth in the dock was 25 ft 6 in. To expedite the handling of coal for shipment, wagons were hoisted from quay level to loading chutes, all operated hydraulically.

The expected trade, anticipated as being brought to the docks by the North Eastern Railway, did not materialize and the dock company sought the assistance of the North British Railway, then extending its line from Edinburgh to Carlisle; a connection to Silloth resulted. The North British Railway purchased the assets of the dock company in 1880.

Prior to this, in April 1879, the wall on the west side of the dock entrance collapsed, the gate fell and some 60 ft of the west pierhead was carried away; all trade was suspended. Plans for a new dock were prepared by Thomas Meik and Son of Edinburgh, and a contract was awarded to (Sir) Walter Scott & Co. of Newcastle. Work began in May 1882 and the new dock was opened on 30 June 1885.

The new dock had an area of some 6 acres and the old structure was allowed to remain as a tidal basin. The dock walls are of concrete and are 36 feet high, varying in thickness from 17 ft 9 in. at foundation level to 3 ft 6 in. at the top; the walls are provided with granite cappings. The entrance gates were of greenheart timber and were made by Muir of Motherwell; they provide an entrance some 50 ft wide with a depth of water of 24 ft at high tide. The gates were worked hydraulically and hydraulic hoists and cranes were provided by Sir W.G. Armstrong,

Mitchell & Co. Construction of the new dock involved the excavation of more than half a million cubic yards of material. The cost of the dock was estimated as being approximately £100 000.

Sources

ABERNETHY J. Description of works at the Ports of Swansea, Blyth and Silloth. *Min. Proc. Instn Civ. Engrs*, 1861–62, **21**, 309–344.

Carlisle Patriot, 3 July 1885.

9. Maryport Docks

The origins of Maryport date from Roman times but it was not until the 18th century that its later development took place. Land nearby was owned by the Senhouse family and it was largely under its control that the mining and shipment of coal began. In 1749, Humphry Senhouse obtained parliamentary approval for the port's improvement, and a new pier—now the North Quay—was built and the river channel was widened. He also released land for building purposes, naming the new town after his wife. Trade expanded with the export of coal, iron and glassware to the American Colonies and the West Indies.

HEW 965

NY 03 36

To permit increased trade, and to compete with the new Port Carlisle for steam packet services, Maryport obtained an Act of Parliament in 1833 to build a new dock and pier, with a lighthouse. The new dock, which required deepening within two years of its completion, was built on the flat sandbank area south of the river and was completed in 1837. The pier was constructed of timber in 1846, at which time a 32 ft high cast iron lighthouse was erected.

In 1857 the 3½ acre Elizabeth Dock was built, entered from the earlier dock, which then became a basin. In 1867 coal shipments rose to almost 500 000 tons, but then declined as more coal came to be consumed by the local iron industry. Between 1880 and 1884 land to the south of the docks was reclaimed by constructing an embankment and sea wall. A new basin and 6 acre dock—the Senhouse Dock—was formed to the designs of Sir John Hawkshaw and Harrison Hayter, although its entrance was somewhat constricted; the South Pier was also extended. The cost of these works had been more than double that

Maryport
Lighthouse

R.W. RENNISON

expected and, as a result, it was found impossible to make the improvements necessary to accommodate larger steamships. There was, however, a successful period of trading at the end of the 19th century, following which a decline in coastal trading led to the port's end.

Sources

JACKSON N. and M. *A History of Maryport, AD 78–1900*, no date.

HAGUE D. and CHRISTIE C. *Lighthouses*. Gomer Press, Llandysul, 1975, 104.

115

10. Workington Harbour and Docks

Originally a fishing village, Workington lies on both sides of the River Derwent. In early years and under the control of the Curwen family, quays were constructed on the river banks to permit coal from local mines to be loaded for shipment to Ireland; the river was able to accommodate vessels of up to 400 tons.

In the 19th century a local iron industry developed around the mining of haematite iron ore which was present in the area and ironworks were established. In 1856 Henry Bessemer developed the process of producing steel directly from pig iron using a converter and, for this process to be effective, haematite ores were needed, rather than the more common ores. In 1857 the Workington Haematite Iron and Steel Works built blast furnaces, Bessemer converters and rolling mills to produce the first ever commercial quantities of mild steel.

Coal exports grew and were soon joined by the products of the steel works and in 1864 a new wet dock, the Lonsdale Dock, was built to the designs of Alexander Meadows Rendel. It incorporated coal drops, but its alignment was such that the size of ship able to use it was somewhat limited.

As supplies of local ores became depleted it became necessary to import ores from Spain and South America, in turn leading to the need for accommodation for larger ships. From 1923 the dock was reconstructed, enlarged and deepened to the designs of Rendel, Palmer and Tritton at an estimated cost of £500 000. The old entrance was closed and the dock extended westwards to increase its area from 4 to 6.4 acres with a 70 ft wide entrance opening directly from the sea, together with a 700 ft long pier. Piled sea walls enabled land at the west end of the harbour to be reclaimed. Initially, the contractors were Kirk & Randall of London, but many problems were encountered, particularly abnormal storms and rock head levels higher than expected, which affected piling. In March 1926 the company failed, and was replaced by Sir Henry Japp. Construction was completed in 1927 and the dock was opened in March of that year by the Prince of Wales, who gave his name to it.

The steelworks closed in 1974 and coal exports have

HEW 2014

NX 99 29

ceased; the port, however, remains open under the ownership of Cumbria County Council.

Source

Information held by Port Engineer, Workington.

11.Whitehaven Harbour

First used by the Romans, Whitehaven lies in a north-facing bay on the Cumbrian coast. In exchange for the use of ships for his Irish campaigns in the 12th century, King Henry II granted the port to the Prior of St Bees and later, in the 16th century, the harbour was occupied by a small community of fishermen.

Early in the 17th century the harbour and surrounding land, underlain by extensive coal measures, were acquired by the Lowther family, major landowners in the area and later to become Earls of Lonsdale. Sir Christopher Lowther began the export of coal and salt from the port, manufacturing the salt by the use of low-grade coal. To aid this trade, the first of the extant piers—the Old Quay—was built in 1634 by Robert Storey. It was extended in 1665 and 1681 by Richard Caton and a lighthouse with an oriel window was added between 1710

HEW 966

NX 97 18

Whitehaven harbour

AEROFILMS

117

and 1721. In 1693 a rough stone protective breakwater, Mr Lowther's Bulwark, was built as part of a scheme to enclose the inner harbour.

During the 17th and 18th centuries the port prospered and Sir John Lowther began the construction of the town, unusual in its grid pattern of streets. In 1711 a Harbour Trust was formed and the construction of a new pier, the Sugar (Old) Tongue, was undertaken in 1735, an outer breakwater, the Old New Quay, in 1742, and the Lime (New) Tongue in 1754. This period of great prosperity ended in the 1770s with the American War of Independence, which halted trade with both America and the West Indies.

Coal from the Lowther collieries, shipped especially to Ireland, then became the principal export and this trade led to the construction in 1785 of the North Wall pier, so forming a North Harbour as recommended by John Smeaton in 1768. In 1804 Captain John Huddert proposed that the piers be modified and this work was wholly completed by 1823. Suggestions for further improvement were made by, among others, John Rennie in 1814 and William Chapman in 1821; none of these proposals was adopted.

In 1823 Joseph Whidbey and (Sir) John Rennie proposed a new West pier and it was built by Fox between 1824 and 1830. In 1833 Rennie proposed a new North pier and its building was undertaken by David Logan, its completion being achieved in 1841. During construction a shipwreck had led to a reassessment of Rennie's design—discussions had involved both James Walker and Jesse Hartley—and it was Logan who was entrusted with the redesign of the pier's roundhead, built by his assistant, Ebenezer Stiven.

The last of the port's improvements was the formation of a gated wet dock, the Queen's Dock; it was designed by (Sir) James Brunlees and, begun by Joseph Phillips in 1872, was completed by Parry, Kirk and Knight in 1876.

Coal exports from the port continued and peaked in 1928 at 400 000 tons; they then declined, ceasing completely in the 1980s. Following the 1939–45 war phosphates were imported for detergent manufacture but this trade, too, has now ceased.

Sources

Tyson B. Some harbour works in West Cumberland before 1710. *Trans. Ancient Monuments Soc.*, 1985, **NS 29**, 173–208.

Scott Hindson B. *Whitehaven Harbour.* Phillimore, Chichester, 1994.

Engineering Reports held by the Institution of Civil Engineers.

12. Hodbarrow Sea Defences

The sea barrier at Hodbarrow is, in its concept, part sea defence and part an earth dam. It was built to prevent the inflow of the sea onto land which was likely to, and which did, subside as a result of the underground mining of iron ore.

HEW 968

SD 165 787 to 182 781

In 1855 the Earl of Lonsdale had granted a lease for the mining of haematite to the Hodbarrow Mining Company, a result of the presence of a 60 ft thick ore deposit at a depth of 80 ft. From 1873 the ore was extensively worked, with an average rate of extraction of 450 000 tons per annum.

The first protection works comprised 6 in. thick timber

Hodbarrow Sea Defences

sheet piles driven some 6 ft into the ground with main piles 12 in. square to a depth of 20 ft. These defences were breached as the result of subsidence in 1884, leading to further protection being afforded by means of a concrete wall, backed by a clay embankment and made watertight with puddled clay placed immediately behind the concrete. Built between 1888 and 1890, this wall, too, encountered subsidence problems in 1898.

Under the direction of Coode, Son and Matthews, a new barrier was provided and in 1899 the contract was let to John Aird & Co.; work began the following year. Providing for the reclamation and protection of 170 acres, the defences were required to be both watertight and flexible and it is significant that the services of James Mansergh, involved elsewhere in dam design, were secured.

As construction proceeded, problems were encountered as far as ground conditions were concerned and it was necessary to amend the design. Originally, the barrier was to consist of an outer bank of limestone with an inner one of slag while, between them, a puddle clay cut-off would be formed with clay fill above it. The changes involved the abandonment of the puddle clay cut-off and its replacement with, at first, timber sheet piles comprising 12 in. square members, and later with steel sheet piles up to some 30 ft in length; in places, water jetting was used to assist their driving.

When completed, the embankment had a slope of 1 in 1 on its inner face and 1 in 1.5 on its outer and, with a maximum height of approximately 40 ft, had maximum crest and base widths of 83 and 210 ft respectively. Its total length was 6870 ft and its construction consumed 621 000 cubic yards of limestone, 34 000 cubic yards of slag—its use discontinued during construction—543 000 cubic yards of clay fill and 80 000 cubic yards of concrete. The sea was finally excluded in July 1904 and final completion was achieved in October of that year.

Source

BIDWELL H.S. The Outer Barrier, Hodbarrow Iron Mines, Millom, Cumberland. *Min. Proc. Instn Civ. Engrs*, 1906, **165**, 156–218.

13. Barrow-in-Furness Docks

The growth of the town of Barrow-in-Furness is analagous with that of Middlesbrough; both towns owe their beginnings to the exploitation of iron ore and the industry which resulted from its working. The development of the two towns was heavily dependent upon railways and it was, in fact, the railway companies which built the first docks. Both towns grew from extremely small communities, Barrow to 57 000 and Middlesbrough to 91 000 by 1901. The completion of the Furness Railway in 1846 enabled iron ore to be shipped from Barrow in increasing quantities and the discovery of the Park deposit of ore by H.W. Schneider in 1850 hastened the process.

The channel between Barrow Island and the mainland was the site of the first of the town's docks. Their construction had been sanctioned in 1863, at which time the docks were vested in the railway company. Work began in the same year, the contractors being Brassey and Field. The Devonshire Dock, to the west, was 500 ft wide with a water depth of 24 ft and incorporated an entrance basin 500 ft by 150 ft, with 60 ft wide double-skinned wrought iron gates. A graving dock capable of taking ships of 5500 tons was included. The Buccleugh Dock was, in effect, a duplicate of the Devonshire, separated from it

HEW 2016

SD 20 68

Barrow Docks

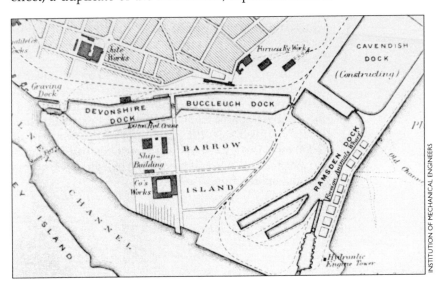

only by a movable bridge. Together, the two docks were slightly over a mile long. The Devonshire dock was opened with great celebration on 19 September 1867— 1100 invited guests were present—and the Buccleugh in 1872. Both docks were designed by McClean and Stileman, the latter responsible for overseeing construction.

To the south-east of the earlier structures, the Ramsden Dock was built to increase the port's capacity and named after Sir James Ramsden, the former locomotive engineer of the Furness Railway who was responsible for the establishment of the town. Sanctioned in 1872, the dock was opened in 1879, also having been designed by Stileman. Its entrance, providing a width of 100 ft, was fitted with wrought iron segmental gates with all dock gear worked by hydraulic machinery supplied by Sir W.G. Armstrong & Co.

In 1904, to accommodate the Japanese battleship *Mikasa*, then building at the works of Vickers, the entrance to the Ramsden Dock was enlarged by lowering its cill by 6 ft and dredging a deeper channel through the dock system. At the west end of the Ramsden Dock, the lock gates were replaced with a sliding steel caisson, built by Vickers & Co. Ltd. The contractor for the work was Sir John Aird & Co. and the engineer Frank Stileman.

The first two docks built at Barrow each had an area of 31 acres and the Ramsden Dock covered 40 acres. Additionally, the Cavendish Dock—used only as a timber dock—provided a further 146 acres; the total area of the dock complex was 450 acres.

The town of Barrow is now dominated by the installation built by Vickers Shipbuilding and Engineering Ltd for the construction and maintenance of Trident submarines for the Royal Navy. It comprises a construction hall together with a ship lift capable of moving a load of 24 000 tons. Design work was undertaken by R.T. James and Partners; the work was executed by Alfred McAlpine plc and was completed in 1986.

Sources

STILEMAN F.C. On the docks and railway approaches at Barrow-in-Furness. *Proc. Instn Mech. Engrs*, 1880, 324–335.

SAVILLE L.H. Lowering the cill of the Ramsden dock, Barrow-in Furness. *Min. Proc. Instn Civ. Engrs*, 1903–04, **158**, 106–119 and 133–153.

14. Walney Bridge, Barrow

Walney Island, some 9 miles long, is separated from the mainland at Barrow-in-Furness by the Walney channel. Following the establishment of a shipbuilding and engineering works, coming under the control of Vickers, Sons and Maxim in 1897, an area of housing, Vickerstown, developed on the island, which was served only by ferry until the completion of the bridge.

In 1905 work began on the construction of a bridge; approximately 1125 ft long in total, with eight fixed lattice-girder spans of up to 117 ft, it incorporates a lifting section to permit the passage of ships. This section comprises two half-span steel plate girders 15 ft 3 in. deep at the pivots and 5 ft at the centre, providing a clear opening of 120 ft. The opening section works on the Scherzer rolling lift principle and is electrically operated by equipment provided by Crompton & Co. Ltd. The mode of operation is that, when opened, the bridge section 'rolls back at the same time as the end rises...(allowing) the same width of opening to be obtained with a smaller angle of rotation'. The bridge is 50 ft wide between parapets and all piers, including those of the fixed spans, are carried on concrete-filled twin cylinders connected by capsill girders; the cylinders are up to 18 ft 6 in. diameter at their bases and were sunk, using compressed air working, to a maximum depth of 62 ft below high water.

HEW 2015

SD 189 686

At the time of the bridge's completion it was written that there were only four such bridges in Britain. The Walney Bridge was designed by Sir Benjamin Baker and C. A. Hurtzig with E. M. Wood undertaking the detailed design; it was built by Sir William Arrol & Co. Ltd.

Source

TREWBY A. Walney Bridge, Barrow-in-Furness. *Min. Proc. Instn Civ. Engrs*, 1910, **182**, 265–281.

15. Kent and Leven Viaducts

The Ulverstone and Lancaster Railway was connected with the Lancaster and Carlisle Railway at Carnforth in 1857. The main engineering works on it were two long viaducts, one crossing the River Leven near Ulverston

HEW 964

SD322 787

HEW 963

SD453 792

Leven Viaduct

and the other the River Kent at Arnside. Both have a considerable number of short spans: Leven had 48 at 30 ft centres and Kent 50 at 30 ft centres. Each had a telescopic opening span of 36 ft and the track was at a height of 26 ft.

The engineer was (Sir) James Brunlees and to deal with difficult ground conditions involving sands and silts to a depth of 70 ft he used cast iron piles and 10 in. diameter columns with large discs at their bases. To assist driving, the piles were jetted and were later filled with concrete. Initially there were four columns per pier for a single track railway, but the number was increased to six when the second track was added in 1863. The cast iron columns deteriorated in the estuarine conditions and the piles were enclosed in brickwork and concrete in about 1915. The original wrought iron lattice girders, one under each rail, were replaced between 1885 and 1887 and some spans have been altered.

The contractors for the Leven crossing were W. & J. Galloway of Manchester and for the Kent crossing James Featherstone, also of Manchester.

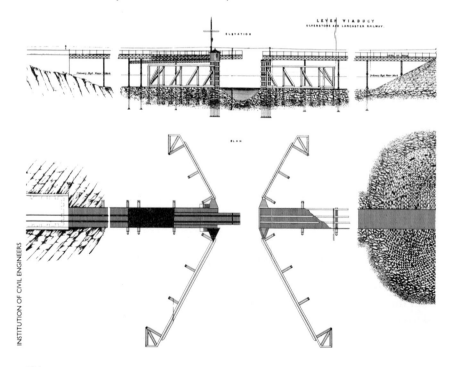

Sources

BRUNLEES J. Descriptions of the iron viaducts erected across the tidal estuaries of the Rivers Kent and Leven in Morecambe Bay for the Ulverstone and Lancaster Railway. *Min. Proc. Instn Civ. Engrs*, 1858, **17**, 442–445.

ALEXANDER J. Reconstruction of Kent and Leven viaducts. Furness section of the LM & S Railway. *Min. Proc. Instn Civ. Engrs*, 1930, **230**, 125–142.

16. Nent Force Level

During the 18th century, and well into the 19th, lead mining was a thriving industry in the North Pennine orefield. The terrain there was such that many mines could be drained by means of a 'level', an access and haulage tunnel driven almost horizontally to the workings from a valley side.

In 1776, John Smeaton was one of the receivers of the Greenwich Hospital Estates, owners of considerable areas of land in the North Pennines and much involved in lead mining there. At that time, the decision was made to drive a level from Alston to Nenthead, some 5 miles distant. It was hoped that hitherto unknown veins of ore might be discovered, but in the event nothing of significance was found.

HEW 398

NY 719 468 to 783 436

The tunnel was driven from a single face, and initially it was planned that it should be 7 ft high and some 3 ft wide. In 1777, after discussions had taken place with John Gilbert, who was involved with the Duke of Bridgewater at Worsley and a lessee of lead mines in the Alston area, it was decided that the tunnel's dimensions should be increased. The revised size was 8 ft in both height and width, so enabling boats to be used to carry ore from the underground workings; a water depth of 4 ft was envisaged.

The level was never completed in the form intended and work on it temporarily ceased in 1842 after some £80 000 had been spent. The level was extended between 1870 and 1904, but the new drivings were also unsuccessful so far as the discovery of ore bodies was concerned. The level is now accessible only with difficulty by means of shafts along its length.

A similar tunnel, the Blackett Level, was later driven

to run from Allendale to Allenheads, although it was never intended that it should serve as an underground canal. In this instance, the engineers were Thomas Sopwith and Thomas John Bewick and the level's cross-section was smaller, 8 ft high and 5 ft wide. Perhaps reflecting improvements in surveying, the later tunnel was driven from five shafts and work on it began in 1855; uncompleted, it was abandoned in 1903. The tunnel portal is visible by the side of the river near Allendale (NY 835 557).

Source

WILSON P. The Nent Force Level. *Trans. Cumbria and Westmorland Antiqu. Archaeol. Soc.*, 1963, **63**, 253–280.

17. Thirlmere Reservoir

The first impounding scheme for the supply of water to Manchester was the construction of the Lower Gorton Reservoir in 1825. Further reservoirs followed and in 1874 John Frederic Bateman advised Manchester's Waterworks Committee that the Longdendale reservoirs, which were nearing completion, would be adequate to meet the rising demand for water without restriction for only a further seven years. He strongly recommended that the city should look to Ullswater for a substantial supply, hinting at the possibility of Newcastle viewing that lake as a possible source. Further consideration, however, led to the Thirlmere scheme being developed.

HEW 607

NY 308 189

The overflow cill of Thirlmere Reservoir is 53 ft above the average level of the original twin lakes and the volume of water impounded is 8900 million gallons. The almost inconspicuous two-part concrete and masonry dam is 857 ft long with a maximum height of 66 ft, but with foundations as much as 58 ft below the present toe level.

The dam was built between 1890 and 1894 and its hearting inside the masonry faces is of rock 'plums' embedded in concrete. Unlike other solid dams of that era, in which the overflow formed an integral part of the dam structure, the overflow at the west end of the dam is of a swallow-hole form of construction and matches the dam in its seclusion. Water is taken to Manchester, 100 miles away, through a draw-off well near the southern end of the reservoir, feeding into a tunnel under Dunmail Raise. The dam was designed by George Henry Hill, who had been in partnership with Bateman, and was built by Morrison and Mason of Glasgow.

Sources

HILL G.H. The Thirlmere Works for the water supply of Manchester. *Min. Proc. Instn Civ. Engrs*, 1896, **126**, 2–23.

HOYLE N. and SANKEY K. *Thirlmere Water—a hundred miles, a hundred years*. Centwrite, Bury, Lancs., 1994.

18. Haweswater Reservoir

In common with many water undertakings, Manchester needed to develop sources ahead of a rising demand for water and Haweswater Reservoir was built to this end between 1934 and 1941 under the direction of the engineer to the Water Department, Lewis Holme Lewis, using direct labour. William Hope Masterton Jameson was resident engineer and George Eric Taylor designed the hollow buttress concrete dam, a rare British example of this form of structure and technically ahead of its time.

The dam consists of 44 units, each 35 ft long and

HEW 181

NY 504 157

Haweswater Reservoir

NORTH WEST WATER PLC

generally I-shaped in section, each being stable and independent of its neighbours, to which it is linked only by watertight contraction/expansion joints; thus a series of caverns, linked by walkways through the webs, was formed within the dam. This form of construction produces high ground pressures, but it was made possible here by the very strong andesite rock which extends across the valley. The structure is entirely of plain concrete with a maximum height above foundation of 120 ft, raising the original level of the lake by 96 ft and creating a reservoir of 18 600 million gallons capacity. Although the Act which authorized construction provided for an 8 mile railway from the main line to bring in construction materials, this was actually achieved by the construction of a concrete road.

The inflow from the direct catchment was supplemented between 1955 and 1967 by stream intakes, contour aqueducts and tunnels from Swindale, Wet Sleddale and Heltondale; this scheme for utilizing all the tributary streams of the River Lowther had been devised by G.H. Hill & Sons for the 1919 Act. A plain mass concrete dam 70 ft high at Wet Sleddale was completed in 1967. Since 1971, additional water has been pumped, when conditions allow, from Ullswater and brought into Haweswater, using the aqueduct from Heltondale. The dependable yield of Haweswater and its catchwater supplements, after the release of compensation water, is 66 million gallons per day, to which figure Ullswater now adds 25 million gallons per day.

Source

TAYLOR G. The Haweswater Reservoir. *J. Instn Water Engrs*, 1951, **5**, 355–399.

19. Station Road Bridge, Keswick

The Cockermouth, Keswick and Penrith Railway was established in 1861, the Stockton and Darlington Railway then being authorized to subscribe towards its capital. The completion of the line in 1864 enabled coke to be transported from Bishop Auckland to Workington and, in the opposite direction, haematite ore was taken from

R.W. RENNISON

the Workington district for use in the blast furnaces of Middlesbrough's burgeoning iron trade.

Station Road Bridge, Keswick

The bridge at Keswick carries a road over the River Greta to provide access between town and station. Initially it comprised three cast iron arch ribs at 11 ft 3 in. centres with a span of 58 ft 6 in., but it was widened circa 1900 to give its present width of 36 ft 6 in.

HEW 1038

NY 268 235

Designed by (Sir) Thomas Bouch, the bridge's castings originated from the works of Gilkes & Co. of Middlesbrough. The widening of the bridge, when three steel ribs were inserted to replace the damaged centre iron rib, was carried out by the Workington Bridge & Boiler Company. The railway closed between Workington and Keswick in 1966 and part of its route westwards from Keswick was used for the A66(T) road, completed in 1977.

Source

TOMLINSON W.W. *The North Eastern Railway*. Longmans Green, London, 1914, 595.

20. Satterthwaite Bridge

HEW 1749

SD 337 921

This bridge, forming a road crossing of the Grizedale Beck, is one of the earliest Hennebique-type reinforced concrete bridges in England, having been designed, as were many of the early similar structures, by L.G. Mouchel. It was built by the Yorkshire Hennebique Company Ltd and was completed in 1905.

It is a single skew span of 42 ft, a true span of 28 ft, with masonry abutments perhaps backed by mass concrete; the parapets are of cut Lakeland stone, rag-faced with sandstone string course and copings. The radius of the intrados is 85 ft and that of the extrados 93 ft, giving an arch thickness of 12 in. at the crown and some 16 in. at the springing. The rise of the arch is 4 ft and small diameter radii have been provided, the appearance of the arch thus being semi-elliptical.

Quite heavily reinforced, the bridge is interesting in that it is an example of a new material, reinforced concrete, being used almost in the manner of its predecessor, masonry.

21. Newby Bridge

HEW 677

SD 369 863

The River Leven is the southern outflow from Lake Windermere and at Newby Bridge, near Lakeside, it is spanned by one of the best ancient road bridges in the district. It has five segmental arches with massive cut-waters and triangular recesses at road level; the spans vary from 17 ft 3 in. to 25 ft 6 in.

The earliest known reference to the bridge is that on Saxton's map of 1577, where it is referred to as the 'new bridge'. Its designer is not known.

22. Devil's Bridge, Kirkby Lonsdale

HEW 147

SD 616 782

For some six centuries the River Lune has been crossed at Kirkby Lonsdale by a structure known as the Devil's Bridge, supposedly built by the monks of St Mary's Abbey, York, the owners of lands to the west. It comprises three spans, two of 55 ft and one of 28 ft and its height, from parapet to water, is 45 ft. Each arch exhibits four

R.W. RENNISON

Devil's Bridge

ribs, the same type of construction as is found at Twizel, and Jervoise refers to it as 'the finest bridge in the North of England, although Twizel Bridge...is nearly as impressive'. With its width between parapets of only 11 ft 7 in., the bridge was closed to vehicular traffic in 1932.

Source

JERVOISE E. *The ancient bridges of the North of England*. The Architectural Press, London, 1931, 113 and 131.

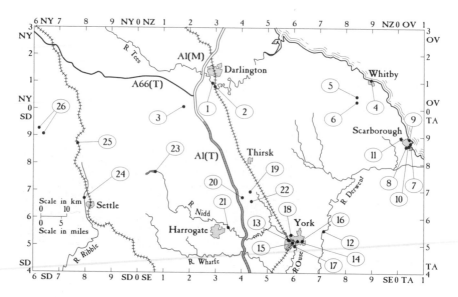

1	Croft Bridge
2	Croft Viaduct
3	Richmond Station and Bridge
4	Whitby Harbour
5	Grosmont Horse Tunnel
6	Scales Bridge, Goathland
7	Scarborough Harbour
8	Spa Bridge, Scarborough
9	Scarborough Cliff Railways
10	Scarborough Station Roof
11	Sea Cut, Scalby
12	Stamford Bridge Viaduct
13	Gaunless Bridge
14	York Old Station
15	York Station, 1877
16	Lendal Bridge, York
17	York City Bond
18	York Waterworks
19	Thornton Bridge
20	Cast Iron Bridge, Milby Cut
21	Knaresborough Viaduct
22	Myton-on-Swale Bridge
23	Scar House Dam
24	Stainforth Packhorse Bridge
25	Settle and Carlisle Railway
26	Lune and Rawthey Bridges

5. York and North Yorkshire

Stretching from the North Sea to the Pennines, with its approximate boundaries the River Tees to the north and the River Wharfe to the south, the area of North Yorkshire is predominantly agricultural in its character.

From the early years of the Roman occupation of Britain York was a regional capital, and later it came to be the centre of government of the northern province of the Church of England and the headquarters of the Archbishop of York. It also became a railway centre of some importance and, from 1854, the headquarters of the North Eastern Railway, the strategic force

William Chapman (1750–1832)

behind the development of the ports of the Northumberland and Durham coalfield and perhaps the most monopolistic of the railway companies.

From Roman times York had been a port with access to the sea via the Humber. Apart from this outlet, there were others, among them Whitby and Scarborough, although fishing was a further reason for their existence. Both ports have a history of development from at least the 16th century; both towns became resorts as well, a move accelerated at Scarborough and initiated at Whitby by the coming of the railways.

The railways were central to York's growth. It lay on the main route northwards from London, a route eminently suitable as a result of the nature of the area's topography, necessitating little in the way of cuttings or embankments. The railway came to provide a transport system superior to that provided by the rivers, as the increasing size of vessels made river navigation less economical. As a railway centre York also came to possess an engineering industry, one of few in the area.

A further feature of the north-eastern extremity of the county was the presence of mineral deposits. Ironstone came to be worked extensively, but its mining led more to the development of the River Tees than it did to the prosperity of York. There were also lead ores present in the Pennines, in Swaledale, but the outlet for this trade, too, was the more convenient River Tees. Iron deposits did, however, result in the establishment of an ironworks at Grosmont, west of Whitby, the only one in the county and served by the railway there.

York Old Station in 1861

R.W. RENNISON

1. Croft Bridge

Croft Bridge

HEW 208

NZ 290 098

Before the construction of Blackwell Bridge all traffic travelling south from Darlington used the bridge at Croft. Although an earlier structure was noted in 1356, the present one dates from the 15th century. It has seven arches, pointed in shape, six of them with narrow ribs; five of the arches are of 37 ft span and the other two smaller. The bridge was widened on its upstream side in 1795. The parapets are corbelled out and are supported by carved heads on the downstream side.

2. Croft Viaduct

HEW 572

NZ 291 091

The Great North of England Railway was founded in 1836 to run from York to Newcastle and, with Thomas Storey as engineer, work began the following year. The line was opened as far north as Darlington in 1841, at which time Robert Stephenson took over the duties of Storey, who had resigned, according to Tomlinson, as a result of 'the failure of several bridges on the line'.

Of the civil engineering works, the most significant was the crossing of the River Tees at Croft where a viaduct designed by Henry Welch was built by Deas and

Croft Viaduct

Hogg. The viaduct is 471 ft long and is approximately 50 ft high; its four arches span 45 ft square or 59 ft when the 49° skew is taken into account. The viaduct is built on the line of the earlier Croft branch of the Stockton and Darlington Railway, and its construction, begun in 1833—before the formation of the railway company—took seven years to complete.

Sources

TOMLINSON W. W. *The North Eastern Railway*. Longmans Green, London, 1914, 349–351.

3. Richmond Station and Bridge

The Great North of England Railway was taken over by the Newcastle and Darlington Junction Railway in 1846, at the same time becoming the York and Newcastle Railway. In 1845 powers had been obtained for a branch line from Eryholme to Richmond and this work was completed in 1846.

HEW 618

NZ 177 008

Richmond Station was designed by George T. Andrews. There are two 30 ft spans, each of nine bays. The trusses have only three vertical members and the cast iron arcades between the eight cast iron columns are Gothic

R.W. RENNISON

style with ornate spandrels; the ironwork was supplied by John Walker of York. The branch line closed in 1969 and the station buildings were converted to other use.

Because the station is on the opposite side of the River Swale to the town, the railway company, unusually, provided a bridge for access, a situation similar to that at Keswick. It comprises four spans of approximately 52 ft; its masonry arches are of pointed form, and its 30 ft width between parapets provided a 20 ft roadway and two footpaths. The parapets incorporate corbelled mock arches on the exterior face with decorated pillars at the abutments and piers. The bridge was built by Elwin and Bulmer and both station and bridge are thought to have opened in 1848.

HEW 2017

NZ 176 010

Source

N & DJR. *Committee of Management: Minutes*, 24 June 1847. Public Records Office, Kew, RAIL 772.1.

Richmond Station Bridge

R.W. RENNISON

4. Whitby Harbour

HEW 2020

NZ 90 11

The importance of Whitby Harbour derived both from its being the base for a fishing fleet and its providing a haven for ships in times of storm, especially colliers sailing to London from the ports of the North East. In its early years it was administered by the monks of the Abbey.

It was recorded as early as 1541 that the oak piers protecting the harbour were ruinous, the timber framing being filled only with loose stones. The early piers were replaced by masonry during the reign of Charles I and further work on them was put in hand by Sir Hugh Cholmley circa 1640. Problems continued and in 1702 an Act of Parliament sanctioned the imposition of a duty on coal shipped from Newcastle to provide financial help for the maintenance and improvement of the harbour as a haven; similar Acts followed.

As a result of the dues received, the east pier was built to a length of 200 yards in a north-westerly direction and the west pier to the same length northwards. Under the powers of a further Act, sanction was given in 1735 for the west pier to be extended, but further collapse led to both piers being rebuilt.

In 1781 Jonathan Pickernell was appointed engineer and, following his death in 1812, he was succeeded by James Peacock. In turn, Peacock was followed by Francis Pickernell, who retained the appointment until 1861. Under the first two of these engineers, the west pier was extended to 338 yards by 1814. The bridge over the River Esk, formerly a drawbridge, was replaced circa 1835 by a swing bridge of 45 ft span, built by Hiram Craven & Sons to the design of Francis Pickernell.

In 1845 James Walker reported on the measures required to improve the harbour. He suggested that alterations be made to the piers and proposed the enclosure of the upper part of the harbour, with gates to retain the water, subsequently discharging it at low tide to scour the channel.

A further report was received from John Watt Sandeman in 1880 but it is uncertain whether his recommendations, or any of Walker's, were put into effect. In 1905, however, further work was sanctioned and was undertaken under the supervision of J. Watt Sandeman & Son.

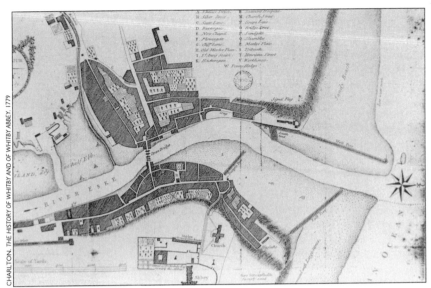

Whitby Harbour
in 1778

Two new piers were built, each 500 ft long and extending from the ends of those existing, a 700 ft long timber fish quay was constructed and the entrance channel was dredged to give an increased depth. In 1957 the fish quay was rebuilt and the harbour wall partially reconstructed.

The character of the town was changed somewhat when George Hudson founded the Whitby Building Company in 1847 to develop land on the West Cliff, an attempt to attract visitors to the town. The establishment of this company coincided with the election of Robert Stephenson as Member of Parliament for the town, a position he held until his death.

Sources

CHARLTON L. *The history of Whitby and of Whitby Abbey.* York, 1779, 313–314 and 327–332.

WALKER J. *The Most Noble Marquis of Normandy, Chairman, and the other trustees of the piers and harbours at Whitby,* 1845.

SANDEMAN J.W. *Trustees of the piers and harbour at Whitby,* 1880.

5. Grosmont Horse Tunnel

On George Stephenson's horse-drawn railway of 1836, built between Whitby and Pickering, quite sharp curves were adequate for the low speeds involved and the earth-

Grosmont Tunnel

M. MURPHY

HEW 3

NZ 827 051

works and structures were minimal considering the terrain. The larger bridges were of timber and have been replaced. This tunnel, 130 yards long and 10 ft wide by 14 ft high, was replaced by a larger tunnel alongside when steam traction was introduced in 1847, but it still remains in use, carrying a footpath. Frederick Swanwick was the site engineer and the portals were given the enhancement of turrets and castellations which, on this miniature scale, is unusual if not unique.

HEW 790

NZ 828 052

A suspension footbridge over the River Esk stands nearby. It has a span of 54 ft and leads to the original tunnel.

Source

Joy D. *The Whitby–Pickering Railway*. Dalesman Books, Clapham, North Yorkshire, 1969.

6. 'Scales' Bridge, Goathland

HEW 826

NZ 831 021

On what is now the North York Moors Railway just north of Goathland is a metal bridge of some technical interest. It carries the line over Ellerbeck, just north of the three-arch road bridge at Darnholme. The original Whitby to Pickering Railway of 1836 included a rope-worked incline at Beckhole, bypassed in 1864 by a 4 mile diversion. This was midway through the era of wrought iron railway bridges, when the use of cast iron had not been quite discontinued and when it was not unusual for a plate girder, a truss girder, or a tied arch to have a cast iron compression flange and a wrought iron tension flange or tie. 'Scales' Bridge is one such bridge which has survived, albeit stiffened by rolled steel channels in the top flange and strengthened in 1908 by the addition of a new steel underslung centre girder.

The original bridge had two outer main girders and underslung cross girders carrying two tracks on longitudinal timbers. The bridge is on such a skew that only half the cross girders are full length. The old main girders are 90 ft long and hogbacked, varying from 4 ft to 7 ft in depth. The bottom flange plates and angles, the web, and the web stiffeners are wrought iron, while the top flange is of cast iron cruciform section in lengths of about 12 ft. There is another similar bridge on the Esk Valley line from Middlesbrough to Whitby.

Source

JOY D. *The Whitby–Pickering Railway*. Dalesman Books, Clapham, North Yorkshire, 1969.

7. Scarborough Harbour

The earliest reference to the provisions made for boats to land at Scarborough dates to the 12th century and in 1546 an Act of Parliament imposed a duty for the repair of the pier, then ruinous. This condition either continued or recurred so that in 1565–67 Queen Elizabeth granted materials towards its repair, or perhaps towards the building of a new structure.

HEW 933

TA 050 887

In 1734 it was noted that two stone piers protected the harbour, 'one of the most commodious of this kingdom'.[1] The older one was built in the 16th century but was extended by William Vincent in the mid-18th century, and was afterwards named after him. The East Pier had been progressively lengthened from the 17th century onwards.

In 1800 the harbour was reported upon by William Chapman, born in Whitby, and under the direction of Matthew Shout, Roger Nixon and William Barry, the haven was improved. The works put in hand comprised the extension of the East Pier by 500 ft, the building and subsequent widening of the West Pier, rebuilding the end of Vincent's Pier, and building a spur 85 ft long from it. The works, all masonry, were undertaken by direct labour until 1818 and then by contract. All work was completed by 1830.[2]

In 1836 George and (Sir) John Rennie produced a plan to build a further large pier which would have virtually doubled the harbour's area, then—and now—totalling some 14 acres. As a result of the expense involved, work did not proceed.

Sources

1. *The Victoria History of the Counties of England: Yorkshire North Riding.* St Catherine Press, London, 1923, 553.

2. SKEMPTON A.W. William Chapman (1749–1832), civil engineer. *Trans. Newcomen Soc.,* 1973–74, **46,** 45–82.

8. Spa Bridge, Scarborough

Spa Bridge, Scarborough

Combining style with simplicity is the four-span carriage drive, now limited to pedestrian use, near the Grand

SCARBOROUGH BOROUGH COUNCIL

Hotel at Scarborough. Multiple-span cast iron arches are rare, and this one dates from 1827. It is said to have been designed by John Outhet, and built by Stead, Snowden and Buckley. It has four spans of 66 ft 6 in. and is 22 ft wide, with four ribs and radial spandrel members similar to the former Dunham Toll Bridge and other bridges designed by George Leather of Leeds. The piers are of neatly panelled and moulded ashlar, again very similar to Dunham.

HEW 211

TA 044 882

9. Scarborough Cliff Railways

Scarborough has been known for its medicinal springs since the 17th century and it later became well known for its sea bathing. In the 19th century its development continued on the higher ground, a fact which gave rise to the need for improved communication between the later development and the sea shore. Britain's first cliff railway was built here, from the Spa to the top of the South Cliff, and was opened in July 1875. It was built by Crossley Brothers of Manchester to a design of William Lucas, a London consulting engineer. It is still in use.

HEW 2018

TA 043 877

The funicular has twin tracks of standard gauge and is 284 ft long with a gradient of 1 in 1¾. Originally there was a single steel rope between the two cars, together with an automatic brake to grip the lines if the rope went slack. It was hydraulically powered by means of water ballast introduced to tanks beneath the upper car, so making the lower car rise. The water was emptied at the bottom of the incline and re-used by pumping to the higher level, at first by pumps powered by a Crossley gas engine and then, from 1879, by steam-operated pumps; in 1935 the lift was converted to electrically powered winding.

A second cliff railway, from a point on the promenade near the pier to Queens Parade, was opened in 1879; repeated slips of the cliffs finally closed it in 1887. The pier was destroyed in a gale in 1905.

A third cliff railway, which still operates, is located between Foreshore Road and St Nicholas Gardens, near the Grand Hotel. It was built in 1869 and is of standard gauge track; it is 255 ft long with an inclination of 1 in 2.

HEW 2019

TA 044 883

The cliff railway was initially worked with steam-driven winding gear, but was converted to direct current electricity in 1920, taking power from the town's tramways system. When the trams were abandoned in 1931, it was converted to conventional alternating current.

Two further lifts were constructed in 1929 and 1930 and they are still in operation.

Sources

LANE M.R. *Baron Marks of Woolwich.* Quiller Press, 1986.

JINKS H.V. and PRICE J.H. A 1975 centenary: the Scarborough cliff lifts. *Modern Tramways*, Apr. 1975, 110–119.

10. Scarborough Station Roof

HEW 454

TA 039 883

The York to Scarborough branch of the York and North Midland Railway was authorized in 1844 and opened a year later. Over the years Scarborough station was extended more than once, but since the end of the steam era has been reduced considerably. It is significant that almost the only roofs deemed worthy of retention are the original ones of 1845.

The station was designed by George T. Andrews and the Italianate colonnaded buildings combine with the train shed, 348 ft long and 88 ft wide. For the standard span of about 40 ft, the wrought iron roof sections are extraordinarily light. The trusses are of the king post type at about 6 ft centres, with 3 in. by 2 in. T-principal rafters, five vertical rods, three 2 in. by 2 in. T-struts each side and two main tie rods rising slightly to the centre post. The covering is diagonal boarding and slates on 1½ in. by 1½ in. angle purlins at 12 in. centres.

Source

TOMLINSON W.W. *The North Eastern Railway.* Longmans Green, London, 1914, 461–463.

11. Sea Cut, Scalby

The River Derwent rises on Fylingdales Moor, north-west of Scarborough, and flows south and then west to Malton before flowing into the River Ouse at Barmby (SE 682 286), a considerable diversion. Some 10 500 acres of land, 12 miles from east to west and lying to the west of Filey, had for a long time suffered from flooding when heavy rain on the moors led to the river's flow being impeded by silt and meanders downstream.

The usual conflicting interests, of mills and farms on the one hand and of navigation on the other, delayed an effective remedy until 1800, when agreement was reached to adopt a scheme proposed by William Chapman for an overflow from Weirhead, at Everley, to the sea at Scalby Mills. The channel then formed, three miles long and known as the Sea Cut, had a bed width of 30 ft and a fall of 135 ft; there are ten weirs and four highway bridges.

HEW 137

SE 972 884 to TA 036 908

The work formed part of the Muston and Yedingham Drainage and under the resident engineer, Robert Wilson, James and Francis Pinkerton carried out the earthworks and John King built the bridges, while the weir at Everley was started by Edmund and Robert Coates and finished by J. and T. Hovington. The Sea Cut opened on 3 September 1804.

Source

SKEMPTON A.W. William Chapman (1749–1832), civil engineer. *Trans. Newcomen Soc.*, 1973–74, **46**, 45–82.

12. Stamford Bridge Viaduct

In 1847 the York and North Midland Railway completed its line from York to Market Weighton, spanning the River Derwent at Stamford Bridge. There are 15 spans with plain semicircular 24 ft brick arches, but the main point of interest is the 90 ft span, six-rib, five-segment cast iron arch crossing the river; it is the oldest remaining railway bridge of this type. Ribs are plain, 28 in. deep with X-type spandrel bracing. The engineer was John Cass Birkinshaw and the contractors Jackson and Bean for the substructure and Gilkes Wilson and Co., of Middlesbrough, for the ironwork. The railway was opened on 4 October 1847, but it is now closed and the track has been removed.

HEW 526

SE 708 554

Source

HUMBER W. *Cast iron and wrought iron bridges and girders for railways structures.* Spon, London, 1857, plates 11 and 12.

R.W. RENNISON

Gaunless Bridge

13. Gaunless Bridge

HEW 190

Now at SE 593 520

This structure is a fragment of the original Stockton and Darlington Railway, opened on 27 October 1825. It was located in the section north-west of Darlington and west of Shildon, which was worked by stationary engines or by horses, isolated between the Etherley and the Brusselton inclines.

When locomotive working was extended westwards to Bishop Auckland in 1842, the Gaunless Bridge was first bypassed and later, in 1901, regirdered. Fortunately, the ironwork was preserved and some of it featured in the local Stockton and Darlington Railway centenary celebrations in 1925. Eventually, with the formation of a new Railway Museum at York, it was re-erected there between 1923 and 1929 and, when that museum was absorbed by the National Railway Museum, the bridge was dismantled, repaired and re-erected in 1975. Although it was then 150 years old and had been assembled at least five times, it had been in service only for a short period.

The bridge consists of four 12 ft 5 in. spans of lenticular trusses on cast iron trestles, with a timber deck. The curved members are of wrought iron, secured by casting into moulded vertical legs which continue upward to support the deck; its method of fixing is by interlocking, not by bolting. The walkways are supported from the trestles on small cantilever brackets, which also lock the main elements into position.

The bridge was probably designed by George Stephenson, but Robert Stephenson may have been involved; it was fabricated by John and Isaac Burrell of Newcastle. The substructure of the bridge remains in situ at West Auckland.

Source

TOMLINSON W.W. *The North Eastern Railway.* Longmans Green, London, 1914, 93.

14. York Old Station

Immediately within the city walls of York stands what remains of the Old Station, a terminus very limited in size and built between 1840 and 1842. There are several features about this station which are notable. Some are attributable to George T. Andrews, some to Thomas Cabry, some perhaps to Thomas Storey, engineer to the Great North of England Railway—for this was a joint station—and some no doubt to the influence of the Stephensons and of George Hudson.

HEW 13

SE 598 517

The first point of interest is that, for the tracks to reach the station, the medieval walls had to be breached. There are two large pointed arches near the corner of Queen Street. The one further from the York Railway Institute carried a footpath on the walls over the York and North Midland Railway. It has a span of 66 ft 3 in. and a width of 6 ft 4 in. and is four-centred. Cabry, one of the George Stephenson team, was the York and North Midland Railway's engineer and he produced a design for this arch, although the alternative scheme of a local architect, Andrews, was preferred. Andrews subsequently built the second arch to serve the station yard, and another one near Lendal Bridge, leading to the Great North of England Railway coal staiths on the River Ouse.

The second feature of note is Andrews' range of offices, serving both the station on its departure side and the railway administration. They are still extant and in use, facing Toft Green, simple but attractive, and surrounded by some of John or W. Tomlinson Walker's gates and railings.

The third feature is the old station roof, or train shed, of cast iron columns, arched cast iron girders and wrought iron trusses in three bays. These bore a strong resemblance to old Euston, the terminus of the London and Birmingham Railway, which is not surprising as, for a time, Euston to York was the main railway route to the north. Cabry in fact visited other stations already built before producing a design for York. A small portion of the York train shed still remains, but is not normally accessible by the public.

Source

TOMLINSON W.W. *The North Eastern Railway*. Longmans Green, London, 1914, 350–351.

15. York Station, 1877

HEW 239

SE 596 517

On 31 July 1854 the York and North Midland Railway amalgamated with the Leeds Northern and the York, Newcastle and Berwick to form the North Eastern Railway. Twenty years later, work began on a new station at York which would not only give vastly increased accommodation, but also permit through running. It was completed and opened on 25 June 1877.

There are three main structures, the train shed itself, the relatively insignificant station buildings and offices, and the hotel, their design credited to Thomas Prosser; after his death in 1874 Benjamin Burleigh continued as Architect to the company. The train shed is built on a sharp curve and has four spans of varying dimensions on three rows of cast iron columns between brick side walls. The main span is 81 ft and the others are 45 ft, 55 ft and 57 ft 6 in. The length of the structures varies between 750 and 850 ft.

The cast iron columns have 27 in. octagonal bases and circular shafts tapered from 21 in. to 18 in. diameter and there are nearly 100 of them in six different sizes; the tops have attractive decorations of acanthus leaves. They are spaced at up to 31 ft centres and carry wrought iron girders with arched soffits, 2 ft deep at the column tops. To these girders are fixed cast iron heraldic panels, and above them are cast iron fretted panels and wrought iron horizontally bowed girders between the roof principals.

The wrought iron arch ribs are fixed-ended plate girders with a rise of about one-third span and a depth at the crown of 14–18 in. The webs are pierced for decorative effect by stars, circles and quatrefoils. These ribs are at about 10 ft centres, every third one resting on a column; the intermediate two rest on the arcade girders, but project below them to meet the ribs in the adjacent span.

The roof covering was originally framed in timber and was a mixture of slates on boarding and saw-tooth roof glazing with wood bars; the latter has been replaced over the years by patent glazing in longitudinal runs. The original heavy wooden end screens with radial glazing bars have been carefully replaced and reglazed with aluminium bars, preserving the radial pattern.

The new station took about three years to build and the roof is considered to be one of the best of its kind: it is of much later vintage than Paddington, which perhaps it most resembles, and 30 years later than Newcastle. Construction was undertaken by John Keswick.

Source

TOMLINSON W.W. *The North Eastern Railway.* Longmans Green, London, 1914, 681–682.

York Station

RAILTRACK PLC

J.A. CARTER

Lendal Bridge

16. Lendal Bridge, York

HEW 209

SE 599 519

The road between the station and York Minster is carried over the River Ouse by Lendal Bridge, designed by Thomas Page and opened in 1863. It has a single main span of 175 ft clear by 37 ft wide in the form of a Tudor arch with heraldic decoration and ornamental lamp standards. It is of cast iron, with six plain ribs each in eleven segments, made by Hawks Crawshay and Co. of Gateshead. Three additional steel ribs were inserted in 1910 to permit the running of tramcars.

17. York City Bond

HEW 357

SE 603 512

Downstream from Lendal Bridge is Ouse Bridge, of three semi-elliptical stone arches, designed by Peter Atkinson and opened in 1820. The original Roman bridge was located between the two. Beyond Ouse Bridge is King's Staith on the left bank and Queen's Staith opposite, where in past years most of the waterborne trade has been handled. Skeldergate Bridge, further downstream, designed by Thomas Page and Son and executed in wrought iron and decorative cast iron, incorporated an opening span to facilitate waterborne transport. Nearby, on the right bank, is a red brick warehouse, the York City Bond, which in 1873 replaced a 17th-century warehouse, a building of less architectural merit, but which survived until about 1968.

A new and better warehouse had been urged for many years, and eventually plans were produced by George Styan, the City Surveyor, in 1872, and the building was brought into use on 26 May of the following year. It forms the three-storey part of the building on the Ouse Bridge side and is about 90 ft by 60 ft, with brick side walls and a line of 8 in. diameter cast iron columns supporting seven bays of jack-arched floors. There are three windows each side, a central opening to the river and a hipped roof on king post trusses.

HEW 355

SE 603 513

In 1875 it was extended towards Skeldergate Bridge in two storeys, about 75 ft square in two sections, one 30 ft wide in two bays with 5½ in. diameter cast iron columns and the other 45 ft wide with 7 in. diameter columns. It would seem that the last boat to unload there did so in 1956. The cast iron work is by Bagshaw and Son of Batley and in one corner of the building there is an interesting cast iron string to wooden stairs.

Source

Duckham B.F. *The Yorkshire Ouse.* David and Charles, Newton Abbot, 1967, 118.

18. York Waterworks, Acomb Landing

The history of the York Waterworks Company goes back to 1677 when Lendal Tower—its origins medieval—was leased by Henry Whistler for 500 years, the agreement then being that a piped supply of water should be provided to the town. John Smeaton later became one of the proprietors of the company and he was responsible for major alterations to the steam engine in the tower, installed earlier as a replacement for the windmill previously used to work the pumps.

In 1846 the company secured an Act of Parliament for a better supply to the town and Thomas Hawksley proposed that an intake from the River Ouse be adopted, upstream from Holgate Beck, and a treatment works built

HEW 216

SE 582 525

there. James Simpson was called upon to design filters at the new works, located between the river and what was then the York and Newcastle Railway; three slow sand filter beds were then constructed, second in England only to those he had built for the Chelsea works in 1828. The beds, some 200 ft by 90 ft and with paved sloping sides, were built by James Darbyshire and Thomas Isaac. Only one of the original filters remains, but others have since been built.

In 1902, four rapid gravity filters were provided, perhaps the first in the country. They were to a design evolved in America and made by the Jewell Filter Company; built with a timber stave outer shell, they survived until the 1950s. A spiral flow clarifier, also to a Jewell design, remains and is thought to be unique in Britain; it forms part of a treatment plant installed in 1937.

The Company also built water towers, two of which should be noted. Near the Acomb Landing works is the Severus water tower (SE 580 519), designed by the Trussed Concrete Steel Company using the Kahn system of reinforced concrete; when built in 1914 to contain 300 000 gallons, it had the biggest capacity in the country. The Siwards How tower (SE 621 509) has a capacity of a million gallons and was built in 1956; it is thought still to have the greatest capacity of any tower in Britain.

Source

HUMPHREYS W.H. The York Waterworks. *Trans. Assoc. Water Engrs*, 1910, **15**, 54–75.

19. Thornton Bridge

HEW 17

SE 433 715

The River Ouse above York is fed by the rivers Ure and Swale, and at Helperby, crossing the Swale, is another example of the work of Thomas Page. The bridge would seem to have been built by John Keswick—who also built York Station—with ironwork by Swingler; it opened on 4 April 1865.

The bridge has a span of 98 ft with four cast iron girders of five segments, forming slightly pointed arches. The ribs are of an unusual twin form and are perforated. The spandrels are X-type lattices with large York City heraldic shields and the bridge's quality is perhaps higher than might be expected in such a rural situation.

Source

JERVOISE E. *The ancient bridges of the North of England*. Architectural Press, London, 1931, 89.

20. Cast iron Girder Bridge over Milby Cut

Knaresborough had at one time a substantial trade in linen. As the River Nidd was not suitable for transport, much of it went by road to Boroughbridge and thence to the River Ouse and so to York. The Ouse is still navigable for seagoing ships as far as Selby, and for smaller craft up to York and beyond. In the 18th century locks were built at Naburn and at Linton, and John Smeaton and other eminent engineers were engaged to continue the improvements still further north. One of these schemes was Milby Cut, formed to bypass a difficult section of the Ure at Boroughbridge and eventually to improve navigation to Ripon.

Milby Cut was opened on 31 October 1769, and was crossed by the Great North Road at the north end of Boroughbridge, necessitating a minor diversion and a small bridge. This bridge was widened soon after 1792 and then duplicated in 1942, so forming a small roundabout, still extant. The old bridge was strengthened then and reconstructed in 1946. The modernized A1 road has since been diverted to bypass the town completely. One of the cast iron girders from the Milby Cut bridge is preserved in the National Railway Museum at York.

HEW 210

SE 395 672 and SE 593 510

The girder is an arched T-beam 18 ft long, with an 8 in. by ¾ in. top flange and a depth of 23 in. at the abutments and 9 in. at the centre; the web thickness is in excess of 2 in. The bridge, when demolished, was 25 ft wide and had ten cast iron girders, with the new intermediate rolled steel joists supporting stone slabs approximately 6 in. thick.

21. Knaresborough Viaduct

HEW 153

SE 348 571

In 1846, the Leeds and Thirsk Railway obtained parliamentary powers for a branch to Knaresborough. Its viaduct over the River Nidd, designed to blend with town, church and castle, was designed by Thomas Grainger of Edinburgh, who was also responsible for the viaduct crossing the River Tees at Yarm. It is a tall, elegant bridge of four segmental, almost semicircular, arches to which architectural detail has been added. The spans of the viaduct are of 56 ft 9 in. and it is 78 ft high. It was opened on 1 October 1851, by which time the company had been renamed the Leeds Northern Railway. Tomlinson states that the opening of the line, excluding the river crossing, took place on 30 October 1848, the line being incomplete because of the collapse of the viaduct on 11 March, when on the point of completion.

Source

TOMLINSON W. W. *The North Eastern Railway.* Longmans Green, London, 1914, 488.

Knaresborough
Viaduct

J.A. CARTER

22. Myton-on-Swale Bridge

Myton-on-Swale
Bridge

This bridge was constructed in 1868 for Major H.M. Stapylton of Myton to connect his properties to Borough-bridge and the North. It has three spans with a central cast iron arch of 100 ft, together with a 20 ft brick arch at either side to accommodate flood waters.

HEW 344

SE 436 667

On the face of the visible arch ribs there are shields with Stapylton's arms encircled by the garter, bearing the motto *Fide sed cui vide*. The three cast iron ribs, and other metalwork, were fabricated by Cliff & Co. of Bradford and the piers, abutments and brick arches were built by Keswick of York.

The design and supervision of the works was the responsibility of G. Gordon Page, under the direction of his father, Thomas, who was responsible for many cast iron bridges, including that at Westminster.

Source

MAW W.H. and DREDGE J. *Engineering*, 1872, 131 and plate LXXI.

23. Scar House Dam

HEW 2033

SD 067 768

The crest road of Scar House Dam is 171 ft 6 in. above original river bed level, and thus, on its completion in 1933, it was the tallest British dam. It is the last of three dams in Nidderdale built by the city of Bradford, along with a 32 mile long aqueduct to the outskirts of the city.

The first dam, Gouthwaite, some 8 miles down the valley, was built between 1893 and 1900 to create a compensation water reservoir and is unusual in that its eastern half is a 56 ft high concrete and masonry overflow section with twin draw-off towers, but adjoined on the west by an embankment.

The second dam, Angram, a mile upstream of Scar House, was built between 1904 and 1916 and is 147 ft high, not including the parapet walls. Between the masonry facings is a hearting of concrete with large stones, 'plums', embedded in it. It was designed by Bradford's water engineer, James Watson, and built by John Best who was a leading dam contractor of that era. To service the building of the dams, the London and North Eastern Railway was extended 7 miles from Pateley Bridge to Lofthouse, and a further 6 miles of private railway was laid to the Angram site.

Scar House Dam was designed by Bradford's next water engineer, Lewis Mitchell, and construction by direct labour began in 1921, a popular approach to dam building by major town councils at that time. A village with accommodation for 600 single men and 62 families, including a school, hospital and recreation rooms, was built at the site, the foundations of the buildings being still visible. Most of the non-mobile plant was electrically powered by a supply generated from the spare hydraulic head between Angram Reservoir and the entrance to the aqueduct tunnel at the toe of Scar House Dam.

The form of the dam wall is identical to that of Angram and it contains 540 000 cubic yards of concrete and masonry. Soft and unsound overburden to the good limestone rock foundation was removed to a depth of 40 ft at the river, stepping up progressively towards the ends, but a concrete-filled cut-off trench 6 ft wide had to be sunk through a further depth of between 60 and 247 ft.

The crest length of the dam wall is 1575 ft but the

YORKSHIRE WATER PLC

Scar House Dam

cut-off trench extends beyond the ends and has a length of 1825 ft. The overflow is of the classic apron spillway form for masonry dams, in ten arched-over sections with a central draw-off tower on the upstream side of the dam. Run-off in a valley to the south is intercepted by a 5½ mile long contour conduit and brought into the reservoir through a tunnel 1800 yards long.

Scar House is accessible by car along a private toll road built over the line of the private railway, but vehicle access to Angram is not allowed. Gouthwaite Dam is on enclosed land but can be seen from the footpath which runs along the former railway on its east side.

Source

Bradford Corporation Waterworks. Scar House Reservoir Works (reprinted from the press), *Trans. Instn Water Engrs*, 1931, **36**, 167–171.

24. Stainforth Packhorse Bridge, near Settle

The masonry packhorse bridge over the River Ribble at Stainforth was probably built in the 17th century. It comprises a single span of 57 ft with a rise, springing to soffit,

HEW 4

SD 818 672

of 13 ft; its width between parapets is 7 ft 2 in. The plain parallel ring segmental arch narrows from 10 ft 6 in. at its springing to 9 ft 6 in. at its crown and its soffit is 17 ft 6 in. above river level. Both abutments are founded on rock.

Source

JERVOISE E. *The ancient bridges of the North of England.* Architectural Press, London, 1931, 134.

25. Settle and Carlisle Railway

HEW 959

SD 813 610 to NY 402 555

The railway between Settle and Carlisle was built as an extension of the Midland Railway, anxious to secure an alliance with the North British Railway. In 1867 the Midland company had almost reached agreement with the London and North Western Railway for the joint use of the Lancaster and Carlisle Railway, but negotiations broke down; this led the Midland company to submit plans to extend northwards its line between Hawes and Settle, to which it was already committed. As a result, the Act for the Settle and Carlisle line was passed in July 1866 and the railway proved to be the last major line in Britain built by traditional navvy labour, at times up to 2000 men being at work on each of the several contracts.

The railway totals 73 miles in length, with its highest section 1169 ft above sea level, and it includes gradients as steep as 1 in 100, a result of its having been forced to traverse the more difficult areas of the Pennines. The northern section of the line passes through relatively easy countryside, but its southern section crosses land which is bare and bleak, with hills in view reaching 2500 ft. As a result, several major structures were required.

HEW 6

SD 760 794

The most spectacular of these major works is the Ribblehead Viaduct, built of limestone from a nearby quarry. It comprises 24 spans, each of 45 ft, and its piers taper, being normally 6 ft thick at the arch springing, but with every sixth pier thickened to 18 ft to prevent progressive collapse. The viaduct's foundations were taken down 25 ft below ground level and the total height of construction, foundation to rail level, is 165 ft. This viaduct was initially constructed by John Ashwell, but his financial difficulties in 1871 led to its being completed by Midland Railway direct labour, but on a semi-contractual basis.

Immediately to the north of Ribblehead is the Blea Moor Tunnel, the longest of the many tunnels on this line; its length is 1 mile 869 yards and it is now the highest tunnel in Britain. Doubts exist as to the number of shafts used in its driving but there were probably seven, three—up to 385 ft deep and 17 ft diameter—being retained for ventilation. As for the Ribblehead Viaduct, tunnel construction was initiated by Ashwell, but completed by the company.

Further to the north stands the Dent Head Viaduct, with ten arches of 45 ft span. It, too, is built to prevent

HEW 672

SD 761 819 to 775 838

Ribblehead Viaduct

EASTERN TRACK RENEWALS

HEW 7

SD 777 844

progressive collapse and comprises two sets of five arches with tapering piers on plinths, the rails 100 ft above the ground. It is 1150 ft above sea level. This structure was also affected by the financial failure of Ashwell.

HEW 8

SD 776 859

The contractors for the section of the line immediately north of Dent Head were Benton and Woodiwiss and it was they who built the Arten Gill Viaduct. It comprises a total of eleven arches of 45 ft span, with stop piers dividing it into sections of two, three and six spans. Built of Dent marble it carries the railway 117 ft above the Arten Gill. Several piers were sunk to 55 ft below stream bed level to reach bedrock.

The railway as a whole was designed under the direction of John Sydney Crossley, chief engineer to the Midland Railway, and it was built as five main contracts, each one with its own resident engineer. Work on the railway began in November 1869 and it was opened to goods traffic in August 1875 and to passengers in May 1876.

Source

MITCHELL W.R. *How they built the Settle and Carlisle Railway.* Cartlebury Publications, Settle, 1989.

26. Lune and Rawthey Bridges

HEW 722

SD 630 930

HEW 723

SD 643 909

The Ingleton Branch of the London and North Western Railway was authorized in 1857 and, under the direction of Joseph Locke and John Edward Errington, it was completed and opened in 1861. To cross the rivers Lune and Rawthey, two identical bridges were built, differing only in their approaches.

Both bridges consist of cast iron arches of 124 ft span, four ribs being used. The arches have a 26 ft rise and are 3 ft 3 in. deep at their crowns. The spandrels are filled with tall round-headed arcades on two tiers. Both bridges are 26 ft 6 in. wide and carried twin railtracks 48 ft above the respective rivers.

The Lune Bridge incorporates three masonry spans of 45 ft at each end. The Rawthey Bridge includes heavy masonry abutments neatly decorated with simple copings, strings and dentil course; it is built to a skew of approximately 40°. Contractors for both bridges were

Coulthard and Allen. Neither bridge is now used for railway purposes. Rawthey Bridge

Source

WESTERN R.G. *The Lowgill Branch, a lost route to Scotland.* Oakwood Press, 1971.

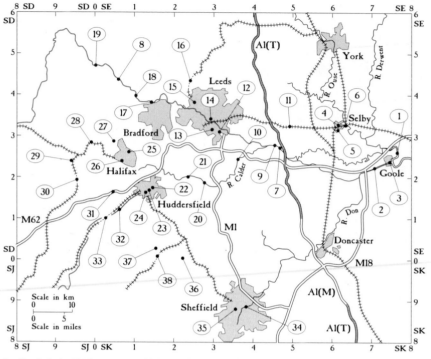

1	Goole Swing Bridge	14 Leeds Corn Exchange Roof
2	Dutch River	15 Cast Iron Arch Bridge,
3	Water Towers, Goole	Newlay and Horsforth
4	Selby Canal and Swing	16 Bramhope Tunnel

1 Goole Swing Bridge
2 Dutch River
3 Water Towers, Goole
4 Selby Canal and Swing
   Bridge
5 Selby Toll Bridge
6 Railway Swing Bridge, Selby
7 Aire and Calder Navigation
8 Leeds and Liverpool Canal
9 Brotherton Bridge
10 Stanley Ferry Aqueduct
11 Leeds and Selby Railway
12 Middleton Colliery
   Railway, Leeds
13 Wellington Street Railway
   Complex, Leeds

14 Leeds Corn Exchange Roof
15 Cast Iron Arch Bridge,
   Newlay and Horsforth
16 Bramhope Tunnel
17 Salt's Mill, Saltaire
18 Bingley Five-Rise Locks
19 Kildwick Bridge
20 Calder and Hebble
   Navigation
21 Cast Iron Bridges, Thornhill
22 Huddersfield Station
23 Warehouse, Huddersfield
   Station
24 Lockwood Viaduct,
   Huddersfield

25 Stephenson-type Girder,
   Halifax
26 North Bridge, Halifax
27 Cold Edge Dams
28 Old Hebden Bridge
29 Gauxholme Viaduct, near
   Todmorden
30 Summit Tunnel
31 Scammonden Dam
32 Huddersfield Canal
33 Standedge Railway Tunnels
34 Norfolk Bridge, Sheffield
35 Wicker Arches, Sheffield
36 Langsett Dam
37 Winscar Dam
38 Woodhead Tunnels

162

6. South and West Yorkshire

Between the River Wharfe and the southern boundary of Yorkshire is an area crossed by the lower reaches of the rivers Derwent, Ouse, Aire and Don. All of them are, or have been, navigable. Underlying them, in the area near Selby, are the coal deposits now being worked from collieries near that town, while further west are the traditional coalfields of Yorkshire which for centuries have served both local industry and export markets, mainly shipping through Goole and Hull.

The natural waterways were improved under Navigation Acts and then augmented by canals over or through the Pennines, which form the western section of the county. Difficult terrain involved the canal companies in the construction of locks and the driving of tunnels and, in the same way, the terrain delayed the spread of railways, which brought with them a large number of substantial viaducts and long tunnels such as Summit, Standedge and Woodhead.

West Yorkshire is perhaps best known for its wool industry. It became centred in the towns around Leeds, initially obtaining power for its manufacturing machinery from the rivers of the Pennines, before adopting steam power. Mechanization brought urbanization and with it the need to construct reservoirs to supply water for domestic consumption, in addition to that needed for power. Nowhere in Britain is there such a concentration of reservoirs as there is in the Pennine regions of Yorkshire and Lancashire.

INSTITUTION OF CIVIL ENGINEERS

Sir John Fowler (1812–98)

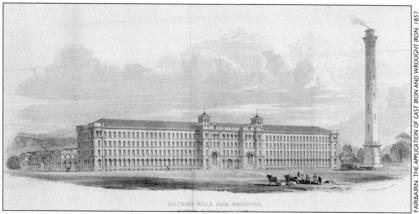

FAIRBAIRN. THE APPLICATION OF CAST IRON AND WROUGHT IRON. 1857

Salt's Mill, Saltaire

Dams for canal purposes had been built in Britain from the 18th century and they were subsequently developed for power and water supply purposes. It was the construction and subsequent failure of two of them in this area, twelve years and 13 miles apart, which was to have a profound effect on dam construction. Bilberry was built to provide water power for a group of mill owners and the dam, 67 ft high, was begun in 1839 and completed three years later. After a chapter of faults and crude remedies it failed in 1852, causing the deaths of 81 people.

The Dale Dyke dam failed much more rapidly. Its 95 ft high earth embankment collapsed in 1864, when the reservoir was filled for the first time; it had been built by a private company for the supply of water to Sheffield. Following the Dale Dyke failure, an inquest was held to investigate the deaths of the 250 victims. Evidence was given by the leading water engineers of the day, among them Simpson, Hawksley, Bateman and Rawlinson, but their views were somewhat inconclusive. The two disasters, taken together, clearly sharpened the awareness among reservoir engineers of the need to deal positively with groundwater, of the need for the tight specification of embankment material and the method of placing it, of the valving systems to be employed and of the need for the rigorous supervision of construction.

1. Goole Swing Bridge

At Skelton, to the east of Goole, the Goole Railway Swing
Bridge carries the Doncaster to Hull line over the River
Ouse. It is probably the finest example of its kind in the
British Isles. When opened in 1869 it was said to be the
second largest railway swing bridge in the world. It has
six sets of three hogback wrought iron plate girders supported on cast iron cylinder piers up to 90 ft in depth to
their foundations. There are five fixed spans of 116 ft, one
at the east end and four at the west end. The swing span
has girders 251 ft long by 16 ft deep and weighs 650 tons.
It turns on 36 rollers, 3 ft in diameter, on a 30 ft diameter
race enclosed in a 50 ft diameter pier, not unlike a naval
gun turret, and is supported on a cluster of seven cylinders. It provides two 100 ft openings for navigation.

It was designed by Thomas Elliot Harrison for the
North Eastern Railway. The fixed spans were constructed
by Butler and Pitts of Stanningley and the swing span by
W.G. Armstrong and Co. of Newcastle upon Tyne. In

HEW 231

SE 765 247

Goole Swing
Bridge

1984 the bridge was damaged, leading to its reconstruction, and in 1988 it again suffered damage as a result of a
collision involving a 35 000 ton ship. The latter accident
moved two of the approach spans by up to 20 ft.

Source

ARMSTRONG Sir W.G. Description of the hydraulic swing bridge for the
North Eastern Railway over the River Ouse near Goole. *Min. Proc. Instn
Mech. Engrs*, Aug. 1869, 121–132.

2. Dutch River

HEW 950

**SE 667 202 to
750 228**

Immediately to the south of Thorne are the Levels of
Hatfield Chase—not unlike the Fens—comprising an
area of peat and marsh, tending to be waterlogged and
difficult to drain. In 1626 Cornelius Vermuyden signed
an agreement with King Charles I to turn this waste into
farmland. Despite great difficulties and local opposition,
he did so with some success, mainly by turning the whole
flow of the River Don, via the north-bound channel, into
the River Aire. Unfortunately, he misjudged the effect of
the tides in the Humber, floods in the rivers Aire, Ouse
and Trent and the concentrated discharge of the Don—
originally with two outlets—on the hitherto untroubled
areas below Snaith. The lawsuits which followed forced
him to cut a completely new channel to divert the Don
away from the Aire so as to discharge directly to the Ouse
at Goole. A sluice was provided but it was washed away
in about 1688 and never replaced. This channel became
known as the Dutch River. As a navigation canal it was
never satisfactory, and was mainly by-passed by other
canals early in the 19th century.

From Ferrybridge and Brotherton the original Aire
and Calder Navigation ran eastwards to the Ouse, via the
Aire, to Airmyn, near the present Boothferry Swing
Bridge. Navigation was difficult in this section and successive improvements resulted in the Knottingley and
Goole Canal of 1826. This ran beside the Dutch River for
its last 6 miles into Goole. Dutch River is now the outfall
of the River Don, a navigable waterway upstream from
Doncaster to Rotherham. Thomas Telford, John Rennie
and George Leather were all involved in this develop-

ment, as was Edward Banks of Joliffe and Banks, the contractors.

There are two swing bridges on the main road through the dock area in the town of Goole, one of which crosses the Aire and Calder Navigation just before it reaches the Ouse. The one immediately to the south of it is known as Dutch River Bridge.

Source

HADFIELD C. *The canals of Yorkshire and North East England.* David and Charles, Newton Abbot, 1972–73, 70–74, 130–132, 209–220, 291–294.

3. Water Towers, Goole

In the town of Goole stand two water towers. The smaller brick tower was built in 1885 to hold 30 000 gallons of water in a cast iron cylindrical tank 30 ft in diameter. The supporting structure is of good quality red brick in English bond, with a plain cylindrical base and tank surround. The shaft is panelled to give a fluted effect and the

HEW 921

SE 741 235

Goole Water Towers

167

tank is roofed by a sheet metal dome. This water tower is now disused but was listed Grade II in 1978.

The larger tower, of reinforced concrete construction, was reputedly the biggest in Europe when built in 1927. The tank is 90 ft in diameter by 22 ft deep with the floor 123 ft above ground level. It is supported on a ring of 24 columns around a 47 ft diameter tower, within which there are four central columns. The tank capacity is 750 000 gallons. The structure was designed by Edward John Silcock of Leeds and built by H. Arnold and Sons of Doncaster.

Source

CASTLE J.H. Municipal works at Goole. *Proc. Instn Mun. Engrs*, 1928, **55**, 605–606.

4. Selby Canal and Swing Bridge

Increasing production of coal and manufactured goods in the West Riding during the 18th century, coupled with the very unsatisfactory state of the roads at that time, encouraged the Aire and Calder Navigation Company to improve its waterways.

The lower reaches of the River Aire were not satisfactory and the opening of a new turnpike road from Leeds to Selby in 1742 not only showed the need to eliminate the ferry across the River Ouse at Selby, but persuaded the Navigation Company to provide a 5 mile short cut from the Aire at Haddesley to the Ouse at Selby. William Jessop was the engineer and the canal was opened in 1778; it was successful for some time, but was outmoded, first by the next Aire and Calder Navigation's major extension to Goole, and later, in 1826 and 1834, by the opening of the Knottingley and Goole Canal and the Leeds and Selby Railway.

Selby Canal is still in use, if not commercially, and the small swing bridge at Selby is one of three to be seen within a radius of half a mile. It was modernized, including the provision of a steel superstructure, in 1977; before that, it was entirely of timber construction.

5. Selby Toll Bridge

Selby Toll Bridge

Not only does Selby Toll Bridge carry a heavy road traffic, but its substructure and protective landing are frequently damaged by river traffic. There was a ferry at this point for 700 years but road traffic was modest, influenced by the volume of shipping proceeding upstream to York. Increasing traffic from Leeds to Selby spilled over to the Aire and Calder Navigation, whose Selby Canal outlet opened in 1778, bringing considerably more trade to Selby.

A census on the ferry traffic in 1790 showed that in one year 105 000 pedestrians, 75 000 horses, 30 000 farm animals and 500 vehicles were conveyed across the river. Subsequently a report was commissioned from William Jessop on the possibility of a bridge and this was authorized in 1791 after an exhaustive enquiry into local objections. The result was the construction of a timber swing bridge, giving a clear opening of 30 ft. It was largely reconstructed in 1970, still on timber supports, but with a steel superstructure with a centrally mounted swing span, providing clear openings of 36 ft 9 in. on either side.

HEW 784

SE 617 325

A model of the old bridge is held at the Science Museum, South Kensington.

Source

MOUNTAIN J. *History of Selby*. Edward Peck, York, 1800.

6. Railway Swing Bridge, Selby

HEW 783

SE 619 324

The third swing bridge at Selby carries the railway from Leeds to Hull over the River Ouse. It was the second opening bridge to take the railway across the Ouse at this site, opened in 1891 to accommodate the east coast main line when the old route via Knottingley was shortened. The main line no longer runs through Selby, since the cut off line was opened in 1983 to avoid the new Selby coalfield.

Designed for the North Eastern Railway under the supervision of Thomas Elliot Harrison, it was built by Nelson and Co. of York, the ironwork provided by the Cleveland Bridge Co. and the swing span machinery by Sir W.G. Armstrong, Mitchell and Co. There are five spans: from the south end, one of 19 ft crosses a road and footpath; another of 15 ft 5 in. crosses over a road; then follow a 110 ft 6 in. fixed span over the river, the main 130 ft swing span also over the river, and a small 10 ft fixed span over a footpath at the north end. Unlike Goole Bridge there are only two main girders, both tracks being carried on full length cross girders.

The substructure for the main spans is supported on cylinders taken down 78 ft to sandstone. The swing span turns on 24 cast steel rollers of 2 ft 6 in. diameter. The cylinder pier is 31 ft in diameter and the main girders, at 26 ft centres, are 130 ft long with a maximum depth of 14 ft 6 in. The unequal arms of 45 ft and 85 ft necessitate a 92 ton balance weight at the north end.

This bridge replaced a cast iron two-leaf trunnion bascule bridge, built in 1839 and giving a 45 ft clear width when open; it was part of the Hull and Selby Railway.

Sources

TRIFFITT J. Swing bridge at Selby, North Eastern Railway. *Min. Proc. Instn Civ. Engrs*, 1896–97, **128**, 207–221.

BRAY W.B. Description of the Ouse Bridge on the Hull and Selby Railway. *Min. Proc. Instn Civ. Engrs*, 1845, **4**, 86–90.

7. Aire and Calder Navigation

The Aire and Calder Navigation originated in 1699 as a river navigation, a ready-made waterway strategically placed to connect the mineral and industrial wealth of the West Riding to the River Ouse and the Humber ports. The River Aire flows through the centre of Leeds and joins the Ouse at Airmyn near Goole; Wakefield, on the River Calder, is virtually on a short branch from the Aire at Castleford.

The Aire and Calder Navigation's history is one of widenings, deepenings, re-alignments and bypasses. John Smeaton and John Rennie were both involved in the construction, while William Jessop built the Selby Canal. By 1820, however, Telford was concerned with a much more ambitious project. The upper parts of both the Aire and the Calder were drastically improved, and the lower Aire was bypassed completely by the Knottingley and Goole Canal and the establishment in 1828 of Goole itself as a port. John Rennie was succeeded on this work by George Leather of Leeds.

The Aire and Calder Navigation terminus at Leeds (SE 308 330) is connected to the Leeds and Liverpool Canal near the City railway station. The river itself is used

HEW 294

**SE 308 330 and
SE 343 202 to
SE 748 231**

John Carr's Great
North Road
bridge at
Ferrybridge, on
the Aire and
Calder Navigation

for the first mile to Knostrop; the next 6 miles to Kippax are in cut; then the river is used again as far as Castleford, 10 miles from Leeds. Here the River Aire continues on its old course, but the main route branches to the left in the Castleford Cut, opposite the River Calder, which here joins the Aire. The Aire is used again past the Ferrybridge power stations and then passes under the former Great North Road where stands John Carr's masonry arch bridge, now disused. The Knottingley–Goole Canal then locks out to the right, but at Bank Dole Lock, 16½ miles from Leeds, there is a link to the river, which is then navigable for 6½ miles to West Haddesley, within sight of Eggborough power station. The Selby Canal connects to the Ouse 11¾ miles from Bank Dole. The Ouse is navigable at Selby by seagoing vessels, although it is 16 miles above Goole, which is itself some 4 hours by water from the sea. The Navigation continues from Knottingley via the 1826 cut through Whitley Bridge and Heck to Goole before being joined by the New Junction Canal of 1905, giving access to the Sheffield and South Yorkshire Navigation.

The other arm of the Aire and Calder Navigation is to Wakefield (SE 343 202), 8 miles from the River Aire at Castleford. There is connection to the Calder and Hebble Navigation at Fall Ings Lock and formerly the Barnsley Canal also joined it hereabouts. The Calder is completely bypassed for the next 5 miles by a cut which actually crosses it at Stanley Ferry. A further 2½ miles takes the Navigation from Woodnook New Cut to Castleford.

One of the notable features of the Aire and Calder Navigation was the compartment boat system, trains of 40 ton metal 'pans' hauled by a tug, 19 or so at a time, and individually hoisted and overturned mechanically at Goole for discharge to ship. The system was pioneered by the Aire and Calder Navigation engineer, William Hamond Bartholomew, in 1862. Pans of various sizes and in varying numbers, both pushed and pulled, have been operated in the past.

Source

HADFIELD C. *The canals of Yorkshire and North East England*. David and Charles, Newton Abbot, 1971 and 1972, 17–43, 121–168, 361–386.

8. Leeds and Liverpool Canal

The Act of Parliament which authorized the construction of the Leeds and Liverpool Canal was passed in 1770, the canal forming, in effect, an extension of the Aire and Calder Navigation. James Brindley and Robert Whitworth were initially involved in the canal's design.

HEW 2038

SJ 339 921 to SE 299 330

The survey for the line of the canal had been undertaken by William Jessop and, after construction began, John Longbotham was the first engineer, with contributions made by John Hustler, Samuel Fletcher, Robert Whitworth and William Whitworth. The first length to be completed was the lock-free section between Bingley and Skipton, opened in 1773.

Initially, the work was let as two main contracts, the contractor for the length between Bingley and Skipton being John Tickle; between Newburgh and Liverpool the contractors were Samuel Weston and John Lawton. It was soon found, however, that the work was beyond them and thereafter contracts were let on a mile by mile basis.

With a length of 127 miles, excluding branches, the canal is the longest built by a single company in the United Kingdom. Work began in 1770 and was completed in 1816. The number of structures is prodigious: there are 106 locks, 56 aqueducts, seven reservoirs, four tunnels, more than 1000 culverts and 588 bridges, 81 of them swinging. Among the individual structures are the Bingley locks, noted below, the 1350 yards long Burnley embankment, the Foulridge tunnel, almost a mile long, and the Wigan locks, raising the canal 214 ft.

Source

CLARKE M. *The Leeds and Liverpool Canal*. Carnegie Press, Bristol, 1994.

9. Brotherton Bridge

The development of the railway system in the area lying between Leeds and Selby, partly by the use of existing tracks and partly by forming links, made it possible for a new route to be made between King's Cross and York. For a time, therefore, the Knottingley branch from Burton Salmon became part of the east coast main line and its crossing of the River Aire at Brotherton, close to what is now Ferrybridge power station, merited a bridge of some magnitude.

The bridge was in fact similar to the Tubular Bridge at Conwy and was built by John Cass Birkinshaw to the requirements of Robert Stephenson; Birkinshaw had worked with Stephenson on the construction of the London and Birmingham Railway. The original Brotherton Bridge, opened in July 1851, had twin tubes 250 ft long, 20 ft 6 in. high, and 11 ft wide, separated by a 2 ft gap and having a lead of 25 ft in order to accommodate the skew. The substructure was appropriately monumental, as can be seen today, although it was altered somewhat when the tubes were replaced between 1901 and 1903 by a pair of 250 ft steel Whipple Murphy trusses at 30 ft 6 in. centres, with 18 underslung cross girders carrying rail-bearers and longitudinal timbers.

The existing bridge was designed by William John Cudworth for the North Eastern Railway and was built by the Cleveland Bridge and Engineering Co. Ltd of Darlington under the supervision of Willoughby Douglas Rudgard.

Sources

TOMLINSON, W.W. *The North Eastern Railway*. Longmans Green, London, 1914, 502, 503.

DEMPSEY G.D. *The practical railway engineer*. Weale, London, 1855, 170–172.

10. Stanley Ferry Aqueduct

The Stanley Ferry Aqueduct carries the new cut of the Aire and Calder Navigation over the River Calder and is thought to be the largest cast iron aqueduct in the world. It consists of a cast iron trough 165 ft long, 24 ft wide and 8 ft 6 in. deep, made up of flanged plates bolted together; it holds 940 tons of water. The trough is supported by some thirty-five $2\frac{1}{4}$ in. diameter wrought iron hangers at 3 ft centres on each side, suspended from a pair of cast iron segmental arch open web ribs at 30 ft 6 in. centres, each in seven segments. The ribs span 155 ft and weigh 110 tons. Each segment is shaped like a five-rung ladder bent to an arc, the T-shaped 'sides' forming the two flanges of the arch ribs, which decrease in depth from

BRITISH WATERWAYS BOARD

springing to crown; the 'rungs' are rectangular and form part of the web. The piled masonry abutments were built by H. McIntosh of London and the castings were supplied by the Milton Ironworks of William Graham and Co., near Sheffield. The engineer was George Leather of Leeds. Construction of the aqueduct began in 1836 and it was opened on 8 August 1839.

Stanley Ferry Aqueduct

The earlier structure was replaced by a pre-stressed precast concrete aqueduct in 1981 and, following its completion, repairs were undertaken so as to preserve the 1839 structure.

Source

BROAD R.J. Restoration of Stanley Ferry Aqueduct. *Conservation of engineering structures*, Instn Civ. Engrs, 1989, 87–94.

11. Leeds and Selby Railway

When the Leeds and Selby Railway Company was formed in 1824 its original intention was to build a railway from Leeds to Hull; as its engineer, George Stephenson was engaged on its design while the construction of the Stockton and Darlington Railway was in progress. Construction was postponed, however, and when the company was revived in 1829, with James Walker as

HEW 917

SE 312 335 to 619 323

engineer, the proposal was for a shorter line to Selby, from which town Hull would be served by water transport down the River Ouse. In a sense, it was overtaken by events as it both failed to penetrate to the heart of Leeds and also stopped short at Selby rather than continuing to Hull, which was not reached until 1840.

The bridges between Leeds and Gascoigne Wood are notable for their graceful semi-elliptical shape and for being built to take four tracks. The elliptical arches are of stone with a span of about 54 ft and were built between 1832 and 1834, soon after the opening of the Liverpool and Manchester Railway and before the London and Birmingham Railway. There are several bridges of this form: that at Garforth (SE 408 335) is easy of access and has an interesting cast iron arched footbridge next to it, one of the standard North Eastern Railway type; there is one near South Milford and three between Peckfield Colliery and Garforth. Two more near Cross Gates show that the case for four-track provision was strong at the Leeds end. There is also an elliptical arch bridge under the railway at Micklefield (SE 446 327) and a larger one over the Selby Road (A63) at SE 339 340.

HEW 345

SE 316 342

West of Garforth stands Shippen Lane overbridge, an early cast iron structure dating from 1834. It has a span of over 50 ft and takes the form of a 60° segment with three I-section ribs 15 in. deep with 5 in. by 1½ in. flanges cast integrally with cruciform-section vertical spandrel posts. It is the last of several on the line and was fabricated by the Stanningley Ironworks.

HEW 234

SE 314 344

At the western end of the railway, the Richmond Hill Tunnel is located near to the Leeds terminus. The original two-track tunnel was enlarged in the 1890s to take five tracks—an unusual procedure—and its length is now a mere 118 yards compared with its original 700 yards. It was originally built between 1831 and 1834 by Joseph Nowell of Dewsbury to the requirements of George Smith, Resident Engineer, on behalf of Walker and Burges of Westminster. The three working shafts, about 80 ft deep, were made permanent by inserting cast iron ellipses 8 ft by 5 ft into the tunnel arch to support 10 ft diameter brick linings. Tinned copper plate reflectors were installed in an effort to light the tunnel and the walls

Selby Station Roof

were whitewashed. Neither lighting nor ventilation proved successful, and it was suggested that much larger shafts, perhaps as big as the tunnel itself, might be required. It is significant that major tunnels such as Kilsby, Box and Bramhope have shafts of diameters greater than the tunnel itself, and it is of interest to note that James Walker stated in 1836 that he thought his were the first permanent shafts ever built. Richmond Hill was one of the first railway tunnels to be used by locomotives rather than rope haulage.

HEW 673

SE 617 323

At the eastern end of the line is the former passenger and goods terminus of the railway, which was closed to passengers in 1840. It comprises an overall timber queen post roof on cast iron columns with narrower aisles. It has a red brick facade with vehicular arches at each side; the openings between them are later. In front, there was originally a landing stage for the onward journey by packet boat to Hull. With the railway, the old Selby station was opened on 22 September 1834.

HEW 518

SE 618 323

Adjacent to the original station is the present-day station, dating from 1891, at which time the re-alignment of tracks through Selby to accommodate higher speeds resulted in the passenger facilities of the earlier stations being removed. The roof of this station comprises cast iron Vierendeel-type girders supported on steel columns, a form used at Hexham and Durham.

Sources

WHISHAW F. *The railways of Great Britain and Ireland.* John Weale, 1842, 2nd edn, 173–184.

WALKER J. On ventilating and lighting tunnels. *Trans. Instn Civ. Engrs*, 1836, **1**, 95–98.

12. Middleton Colliery Railway, Leeds

Not far distant from the River Aire in Leeds is an important element in the transition between waggonways and railways and in forms of motive power. Three miles south of Leeds Bridge is an area of long established collieries with records of mining activity dating back to 1646, and by 1717 the Brandling family, who had mining concerns in the Newcastle area, had important interests there.

In 1758 Charles Brandling received parliamentary sanction for the laying down of a waggonway from his pits at Middleton to Leeds. The Act did not actually authorize construction, but it provided for the compulsory purchase of land for laying down the track, at the same time giving protection to landowners. Brandling's Act for the waggonway was the first such granted, although waggonways—especially in Northumberland and Durham—had been used for the transport of coal from the early years of the 17th century.

The Middleton Colliery Railway began life as a 3 ft gauge line with wooden rails, changing first to a 4 ft gauge with iron rails and then to standard gauge, in 1881, when it was connected to the main line system. Apart from the Act of Parliament, the line was also notable for the fact that it employed the Blenkinsop rack system between 1812 and 1834. The locomotives were built by Matthew Murray, the works of Fenton Murray and Wood being located at Holbeck.

HEW 221

SE 305 307

The railway was closed in 1960, but the former line is perpetuated in a tunnel under the M1 motorway, formed in 1970.

Source

BIDDLE G. *The railway surveyors*. Ian Allan, London, 1990, 19.

13. Wellington Street Railway Complex, Leeds

The Leeds and Thirsk Railway was incorporated on 21 July 1845. It was initially to run between the two towns, but soon after construction began a further Act was obtained to enable it to run to Middlesbrough. It was the intention to share the Wellington Street terminal with the Leeds, Dewsbury and Huddersfield Railway, and a third party to the arrangement was the West Riding Union Railway. Amalgamations involving the several railways led to the choice of depot in its present location.

HEW 2034

SE 294 335 and SE 290 335

The depot was on two levels, the lines being connected by ramps, while to facilitate the transfer of wagons, a wagon hoist—still extant—was provided. The masonry tower (SE 294 335), to lift wagons from one level to another, was designed by (Sir) John Hawkshaw, engineer for the whole project, and was completed in 1854. The hoist principle was not new and had been used a decade earlier by Stephenson and Gooch in the Oldham Road Goods Station at the Manchester terminal of the Manchester and Leeds Railway.

The main feature of the site, additional to the wagon hoist, is the roundhouse (SE 290 335). It is of red brick, a single-storey polygon with gritstone and sandstone dressings. The roundhouse contained a centrally located turntable from which radiated 20 stabling roads with pits, its access being from the east by way of a stone elliptical arched doorway; the turntable was enclosed within the building, but open to the air. The roof trusses are of the composite queen post type with wrought iron rod tension members and timber compression members; at the outer walls the trusses are supported by cast iron corbels. The roof covering is slate underdrawn with tongued and grooved boarding. The building was designed by Thomas Grainger and was completed in 1847.

Contemporary with the roundhouse is a range of buildings running parallel with the canal adjoining the site, envisaged as repair shops for the Leeds and Thirsk Railway. The buildings are architecturally similar to the roundhouse and together they form the first phase of the site's development. Further building subsequently took place, principally the construction of a semi-roundhouse, which although not dated with certainty, is shown on a site plan of 1853.

The group of buildings makes up a complex of some significance and forms the only surviving monument to 19th-century railway development in Leeds, a location of great importance in railway history, with the early establishment of the Middleton Railway, the use of steam traction and the growth of locomotive building.

Source

FITZGERALD R. *Railway complex—Wellington Street.* Unpublished account, 1995.

14. Leeds Corn Exchange Roof

HEW 242

SE 304 334

The roof of the Corn Exchange in Leeds was built by Butler and Co. of Stanningley to the requirements of Cuthbert Brodrick, the architect who designed Leeds Town Hall and the Grand Hotel at Scarborough. It stands near the junction of Briggate and Boar Lane, along Duncan Street, and replaced an earlier building in 1867. It is elliptical in plan, 190 ft long and 136 ft wide, with a most impressive domed roof soaring to a height of 75 ft; its intersecting radial and concentric members create the appearance of an inverted basket. It has 19 main ribs of semi-elliptical form, crossed by semicircular ribs of light section above and below, with longitudinal boarding

above. There is a slated roof and a very large oval roof light.

Leeds Corn
Exchange

Source

LINSTRUM D. *Historic architecture of Leeds*. Oriel Press, Leeds, 1969.

15. Cast Iron Arch Bridge, Newlay and Horsforth

This attractive bridge carries a minor road over the River Aire in the outskirts of Leeds. It was cast in 1819 by Aydon and Elwell of Shelf Ironworks near Bradford, which firm later became part of the Low Moor Ironworks. Built as a toll bridge connected with the Micklethwaite Estate, it was taken over in 1880 jointly by the Midland Railway and the Horsforth Council; it provides access to Newlay and Horsforth Station. The Newlay Bridge carries a road of 10 ft width, together with two footways each 3 ft wide. The 82 ft span has four segmental cast iron ribs each in three sections on pin-type bearings. The spandrels have plain radials leaving six openings of rhomboid shape in each casting. The bridge is similar to Scarbor-

HEW 189

SE 239 368

Newlay Bridge

I.G. JAMES

ough Spa Bridge and the former Dunham Toll Bridge over the River Trent.

16. Bramhope Tunnel

HEW 16

SE 242 408 to
256 438

Bramhope Tunnel is 2 miles 241 yards long and has a maximum depth of some 290 ft. It cuts through the ridge separating the Aire and the Wharfe valleys and was built between 1845 and 1849 for the Leeds and Thirsk Railway, later to become the Leeds Northern Railway.

The engineer was Thomas Grainger of Edinburgh and the contractor James Bray of Leeds. Work was difficult; 2300 men and 400 horses were employed and 1600 million gallons of water had to be pumped from the workings. The strata vary from hard sandstone at the south end, through shales, to clay at the north end, and they dip southwards; there are seven major faults towards the centre of the bore. The tunnel is on a falling gradient northwards and had at least 34 working faces; four were

made into permanent ventilation shafts of large size, 40 ft
by 30 ft, greater than the tunnel's dimensions, 25 ft 6 in.
wide and 25 ft high.

Most of Grainger's work displays a very high quality
of masonry and the portals at Bramhope are no exception.
That at the south end, near Horsforth, is comparatively
plain, but in some ways the more striking. The northern
portal, near Arthington, is well known for its two castle-
like towers, one large—at one time used as a residence—
and one smaller, with the tunnel mouth between them,
surmounted by the Company's heraldic device. To commemorate the men who died during construction a me-
morial in the form of the portal stands in Otley
churchyard.

Source

TOMLINSON W.W. *The North Eastern Railway.* Longmans Green, London,
1914, 500.

Bramhope Tunnel

M.F. BARBEY

17. Salt's Mill, Saltaire

HEW 87

SE 141 381

Sir Titus Salt was one of the great names in the wool industry of the West Riding of Yorkshire. After initial success in Bradford itself, he decided to build a new factory in pleasant surroundings near Shipley, a few miles north of Bradford, set between the Midland Railway and the Leeds and Liverpool Canal. Lockwood and Mawson were the architects and (Sir) William Fairbairn the engineer. Salt and Lockwood visited London in 1851 with a view to purchasing some of the buildings used for the Great Exhibition. They did not prove to be suitable for the weight and vibration of the machinery, so a design was evolved for a more solid construction.

On the south side of the site is the six-storey main block, an attractive building in light stone, 545 ft long, 50 ft wide and 72 ft high. There are long lines of tall square-headed windows broken near the centre by two Italianate towers, between which is the engine house; there are smaller towers at the extremities. The upper floor, continuous across the engine house, was said at the time of building to be the largest room in Europe.[1]

Behind the main building is the 330 ft long warehouse with a T-shaped cross piece at the north end. Two- and three-storey extensions to east and west mask the 330 ft long single-storey glass-roofed weaving shed on the east side, built for 1200 looms, and to the west the 210 ft by 112 ft combing shed, behind the two-storey office block.

The mill building was designed by Fairbairn to be fire-resistant. The walls are load-bearing and the floors are supported on them and on cast iron columns; located approximately along the centre line of the building, the columns provide beam spans of 27 ft and 23 ft. The cast iron beams are spaced at 8 ft 6 in. centres and arches are built between them, the soffits formed of hollow bricks, concreted above. The iron beams are held in position by wrought iron spacing rods and have unequal flanges, the larger one at the bottom.[2]

Sources

1. BALGARNIE REVD. R. *Sir Titus Salt (Bart)*. Hodder and Stoughton, London, 1877. Reprinted by Brenton Publishing Co., Settle, 1970.

2. FAIRBAIRN W. *The application of cast iron and wrought iron to building purposes*. Weale, London, 1857, plate II.

18. Bingley Five-Rise Locks

The Bingley Locks are not the only staircase locks in Britain, but they are perhaps the best known. They are part of a flight of eight, two separate structures fairly close together, one with three locks and the other with five. The latter flight raises the canal almost 60 ft. The locks permit vessels 72 ft long and 14 ft wide to use the canal and they stand in a valley which has the River Aire,

HEW 86

SE 107 398

Bingley Five-Rise Locks.

BRITISH WATERWAYS BOARD

185

the A650 road, the former Midland Railway and a canal running parallel and close together.

The first section of the Leeds and Liverpool Canal, of which the locks form a part, was opened from Bingley to Skipton on 6 April 1773, and on 21 March 1774 'several thousand spectators witnessed the descent of the five-rise at Bingley by five laden boats'.

Source

HADFIELD C. and BIDDLE G. *The canals of North West England*. David and Charles, Newton Abbot, 1970, 74.

19. Kildwick Bridge

HEW 949

SE 011 457

Of the many ancient road and packhorse bridges in Yorkshire, perhaps that at Kildwick on the A629, between Keighley and Skipton, is one of the best. In 1752 it was described as a very old bridge with ribbed arches of hewn stone and with a 'causey' at the south end. The latter was 220 yards long and the bridge itself 46 yards long.

The two northern arches are pointed and of 18 ft and 19 ft span, while the two main spans over the River Aire are segmental, of 29 ft and 33 ft span. The bridge dates from about 1306 and is listed Grade I. It has been widened on its downstream side and is still in use.

Source

CARR J. *Book of bridges*, 1752.

20. Calder and Hebble Navigation

HEW 2022

SE 343 198 to 065 237

The Act of Parliament which authorized the construction of this navigation, running from Wakefield to Sowerby Bridge, was passed in 1758. It was the first river navigation for which John Smeaton was responsible and work on it began in 1760 and was completed in 1770. In 1828 a branch was completed to Halifax; now closed, it can still be traced on the ground.

Smeaton was succeeded in 1765 by James Brindley but, after a short period, Smeaton again became responsible for construction work. Under the two engineers, the navigation's 26 locks were completed, rising a total of 178 ft. Originally there were 5¾ miles of lock cuts and 2 miles of contour canal; the length of the navigation is now

21½ miles. When completed, it was able to accommodate barges 57 ft 6 in. long and 14 ft 2 in. wide. In 1770 a trans-shipment basin was provided at Sowerby Bridge, where three warehouses remain, dating from 1770 to 1803.

Lock cuts constructed in the 19th century have had the result of bypassing some of Smeaton's earlier works. The older locks retain his distinctive style of paddle gear, framed in timber and worked with a wooden hand-spike.

Source

SKEMPTON A.W. (ed.) *John Smeaton, FRS*. Thomas Telford, 1981, 103–108, 123–124.

21. Cast Iron Bridges, Thornhill

These two bridges are similar in form and have arches with Gothic style sub-arches used in the spandrels. They carry the former London and North Western Railway over the Calder and Hebble Navigation and the River Calder, respectively. One of the bridges comprises a very skew arch with six ribs of 100 ft span; it is 29 ft 4 in. wide between parapets. The other has two six-rib spans, each of 101 ft with a 12 ft rise. Each rib has five segments, is 3 ft deep, and has a 12 in. wide top flange, an 8 in. bottom flange and a 2½ in. thick web.

HEW 347

SE 232 203

HEW 348

SE 234 205

The bridges were designed by Thomas Grainger and cast by Joseph Butler of Stanningley, Leeds in 1847 and are thought to be two of the oldest cast iron railway underbridges still in full use.

22. Huddersfield Station

The Huddersfield and Manchester Railway and Canal Co. was incorporated by Act of Parliament on 21 July 1845. Tenders for the station were accepted on 9 June 1846 and it was partly opened in August 1847, by which time the London and North Western Railway had taken over. The station buildings were completed in October 1850; they were designed by James Pigott Pritchett and the building work was undertaken by the firm of Joseph Kaye. The station buildings are 416 ft long, with eight Corinthian columns 68 ft high in the central portico,

HEW 240

SE 145 168

J.A. CARTER

Huddersfield
Station

HEW 446

SE 145 168

flanked by colonnades ending in small matching pavilions; heraldic devices are displayed on the wings.[1] Huddersfield Station is considered to have one of the finest
façades in Britain.

After some 35 years it became necessary to enlarge the
station platforms and they were given an overall pitched
roof in iron, a late example of this form. The queen post
trusses have a span of 77 ft 6 in., supported on longitudinal trusses and columns. Initially, the roof was supported
by cast iron columns, but a collapse during construction,
when three workmen were killed, led to steel H-section
columns being used, placed at 19 ft 3 in. centres. The new
roof, erected by Joseph Butler & Co. of the Stanningley
Ironworks, was completed in 1886.[2]

Huddersfield Station was operated jointly by the London and North Western and the Lancashire and Yorkshire railways from 1849 until they amalgamated in 1922.
The building is a splendid example of Victorian design
but, no longer appropriate to modern railway operation,
it has been taken over by the local authority and forms a
worthy part of St George's Square.

Sources

1. BODY G. *Railway stations of Britain*. Patrick Stephens, Wellingborough,
1990.

2. The Huddersfield Station roof. *Engineering*, 1885, **40**, Oct., 385–386.

23. Warehouse, Huddersfield Station

Approximately 100 yards east of Huddersfield passenger station stands a goods and wool warehouse built jointly for the two railway companies in 1883. Its plan area is 320 ft by 160 ft and it is of five storeys with platforms at ground and second floor levels, the higher level reached by means of a hydraulic wagon hoist, in turn feeding to a traverser. The first floor of the warehouse was built as a fire barrier and it comprises brick jack arches on riveted iron joists and girders with columns on a 40 ft grid; other floors are of timber on iron beams, with intermediate columns. The exterior of the warehouse is of red brick, with bands of blue, and there are large cast iron windows.

HEW 2023

SE 143 168

Source

BIDDLE G. and NOCK O.S. *The railway heritage of Britain*. Michael Joseph, London, 1983, 34–35.

24. Lockwood Viaduct, Huddersfield

The Huddersfield and Sheffield Junction Railway was authorized in 1845 to build a line 13 miles long to connect

Lockwood Viaduct

HEW 155

SE 133 146

Huddersfield with Penistone on the Manchester and Sheffield line. It included six tunnels and four viaducts, of which the largest is Lockwood. Designed by (Sir) John Hawkshaw, the viaduct was built by Miller & Co. under John Fraser, the Resident Engineer. It is one of the largest viaducts in the United Kingdom and probably the finest in West Yorkshire. It is 120 ft high and 476 yards long and has 34 semicircular arches of 30 ft span with two larger spans of 42 ft and 70 ft. It contains nearly a million cubic feet of masonry.

Source

HAWKSHAW J. Description of Lockwood Viaduct on the Huddersfield and Sheffield Railway. *Min. Proc. Instn Civ. Engrs*, 1850, **10**, 296–302.

25. Stephenson-type Girder, Halifax

HEW 2021

SE 098 251

Forming part of a railway bridge over Berry Lane in Halifax is a girder of a type which is almost certainly unique in Britain. It is a remnant of a cast iron bridge from some other site, subsequently shortened to form a 62 ft girder and used as an edge beam to widen an existing masonry arched underbridge. The girder, now of two sections only, exhibits the upstands over the supports earlier used to anchor the wrought iron straps, not used in this later application.

Originally, the girder would have been made up of three sections, bolted together end to end by means of flanged joints to form a single span and strapped to form a girder similar to those used on the River Dee Bridge, which collapsed in 1847.[1] Robert Stephenson, and other engineers, had used this form of girder quite widely, but the failure of the Dee Bridge led to an extensive investigation into the use of cast iron for structures of this type and eventually resulted in a cessation of its use.[2]

A bridge of this type was used at Stockton, where it replaced the suspension bridge which initially carried the Stockton and Darlington Railway's extension to Middlesbrough, while another carried the railway over the River Ouse, in York, towards Scarborough. Both were strengthened by means of diagonal timber supports after the Dee Bridge failure.

The finely dressed and rock-faced sandstone of the

adjoining railway arches and the tunnel to the north are characteristic of the West Riding Union line through Halifax to Bradford, its engineer being (Sir) John Hawkshaw. It was built through difficult terrain between 1847 and 1850. The nearby Halifax Station, designed by Thomas Butterworth and completed in 1850, is another example of Britain's handsome classical railway buildings.

Sources

1. SUTHERLAND R.J.M. The introduction of structural wrought iron. *Trans. Newcomen Soc.,*1963–64, **35**, 67–84.

2. *Report of the Commissioners appointed to inquire into the application of iron to railway structures.* HMSO, 1848.

26. North Bridge, Halifax

Between 1868 and 1871 a cast iron bridge was built to replace the six-arch viaduct of 1774 which had carried the turnpike road over the Hebble Brook at the north end of Halifax. The new bridge, itself by-passed a century later but still in use for local traffic, is a rather magnificent structure in Victorian Gothic style. It has ecclesiastical-type buttresses to the stone pillars, semi-elliptical arch

HEW 729

SE 093 257

North Bridge

J.A. CARTER

ribs, perforated with stars, quatrefoils and circles, and two tiers of lancets in the spandrels; the parapets are also decorative but more restrained. There are two main spans of 160 ft with a rise of 16 ft and two approach arches on the town side; the bridge is 60 ft wide. The parapet ribs are of cast iron with the six inner ribs spaced 8 ft 7 in. apart, partly of cast iron, but with the central 52 ft in wrought iron, a design similar to that used by Thomas Page for the Westminster Bridge.

Halifax North Bridge was designed by John Fraser of Leeds, and his brother James. John had extensive experience of bridge construction for railways, starting with the link line from the original Liverpool and Manchester Railway into Victoria Station.

27. Cold Edge Dams

From 1770 onwards, Yorkshire experienced a rapid growth in its wool industry and, as a result, the provision of a supply of water to drive the mills' machinery became of great importance. The need for water led to the provision of bigger reservoirs capable of supplying a number of mills together. One method of financing these larger-scale works was by the combined efforts of a group of mill owners and both Bilberry and the Cold Edge Dams were the result of such co-operation.

In the Luddenden valley, where the brook of that name runs into the River Calder west of Halifax, the Cold Edge Dam Company was formed circa 1806, its purpose being the conservation of water and the construction of a reservoir to feed eventually up to ten mills, principally producing worsted products. Spring Dam was the first to be completed and, although it was not owned by the Company, it was controlled by it; its embankment was raised in 1827 to increase its capacity. Haigh Coat was actually the first to be built under the auspices of the Company and it was followed in 1835–36 by Leadbeater Dam. The capacities of the three reservoirs were: Spring, 4 million gallons; Haigh Coat, 11 million gallons; and Leadbeater, 8 million gallons. Draining an area of 725 acres, the reservoirs fed water to the series of mills in

HEW 2032

SE 043 297

the valley below, the mill owners paying rents assessed on the head of water available for their waterwheels.

The dams were built, at least in part, by Leadbeater and Stansfield, who had earlier been involved in canal construction; it is interesting to note, in this area especially, the progressive development of earth embankment dams for canal, power and water supply applications. Only two of the reservoirs remain, Spring having been abandoned in 1970.

Sources

Royal Commission on the Historical Monuments of England. *Yorkshire textile mills, 1770–1930*. HMSO, 1992, 132–133.

Water Wheels in the Upper Calder Valley. Halifax Antiquarian Society, 1972, 56–61.

28. Old Hebden Bridge

Hebden Bridge, with the older village of Heptonstall above it to the north, is connected to Burnley by the 'Long Causeway'; on the 1300 ft level, it formed an early route of communication. A later, and lower, route from Todmorden to Burnley is also of some age, since the existing stone bridge, Old Hebden Bridge, which was erected in 1510, is said to have replaced a medieval timber bridge. It has three segmental arches of 23 ft span and is 9 ft wide; it leads to a steep paved road towards Heptonstall.

HEW 948

SD 993 274

Source

Jervoise E. *The ancient bridges of the North of England*. Architectural Press, London, 1931, 103.

29. Gauxholme Viaduct, near Todmorden

Arched bridge girders supporting the deck system by means of hangers were introduced into Great Britain by the Leeds engineer, George Leather, a fact acknowledged by Thomas Telford. Several road-over-river bridges similar in style to Stanley Ferry Aqueduct were built in the 1830s, and this design came to be adopted for railway use. George and Robert Stephenson were not slow to adopt the self-contained cast iron arch, so called through having its ends restrained by a wrought iron tie as the bottom

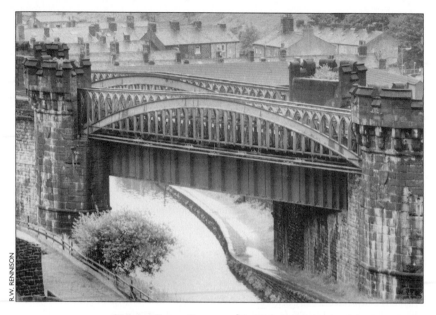

R.W. RENNISON

Gauxhome
Viaduct

chord. The railway tracks were supported by a simple deck system of secondary girders, all hung from the arch.

Several bridges of this type were built between 1835 and 1850, including one over the Regent's Canal in London and another in Derby, since rebuilt. There were three between Manchester and Leeds and, of course, the Newcastle High Level Bridge, where the lower deck is suspended indirectly from the cast iron arches and the railway supported by them. Of the three bridges on the Manchester and Leeds Railway, its engineerGeorge Stephenson, one has been dismantled; Scowcroft (SD 887 065) remains intact but disused at Middleton, near Manchester; and Gauxholme remains in use. From 50 ft at the Regent's Canal, the spans of this form of bridge girder increased to 73 ft at Scowcroft, 102 ft at Gauxholme and 125 ft at Newcastle.

HEW 2

SD 931 233

The original structure is quite complex. The two girders, or trusses, are at 32 ft 8 in. centres, each arch having a pair of cast iron ribs at 5 ft centres, each tied by four rods which effectively form the bottom chord. The arches also have a decorative cast iron bottom chord and an arcade of 34 sub-arches which top the thin columns shrouding the hangers. These arcades are of almost uniform height throughout the bridge's length and they carry a decorative capping which is nearly parallel with the bottom chord. As a result, the whole truss looks almost like a parallel flange open web girder.

The bridge, completed in 1840, spans the Rochdale Canal and is part of an impressive masonry viaduct built on a curve and sweeping down the valley. The appearance of the bridge has been changed as a result of modifications made to it in 1906. At that time, 10 ft deep steel girders were inserted at 20 ft 9 in. centres to relieve the old structure of moving load stresses.

Sources

MARSHALL J. *The Lancashire and Yorkshire Railway*. David and Charles, Newton Abbot, 1969, **1**, 44, 54.

RENNISON, R.W. The high level bridge, Newcastle: its evolution, design and construction. *Trans. Newcomen Soc.*, 1980–81, **52**, 180–207 *passim*.

30. Summit Tunnel

The Manchester and Leeds Railway, with George Stephenson as its engineer, linked the two towns by a route via Littleborough and Todmorden, negotiating the watershed between them by Summit Tunnel, built between 1837 and 1840. At that time it was the longest railway tunnel in Britain, 1 mile 1125 yards long, and the first of the major trans-Pennine tunnels.

HEW 1003

SD 940 208 to 946 182

The tunnel is horseshoe in shape, and of 26 ft span to take two tracks; it is brick-lined. Thomas Gooch supervised the work, which included the sinking of 14 working shafts. His brother Daniel worked on it for a short time before joining the Great Western Railway, where he achieved fame as its locomotive engineer. The contractor was John Stephenson, who was later a partner of William Mackenzie and Thomas Brassey on the Lancaster–Carlisle Railway.

Sources

BLOWER A. *British railway tunnels*. Ian Allan, London, 1964, 40, 105.

MARSHALL J. *Lancashire and Yorkshire Railway*. David and Charles, Newton Abbot, 1969, **1**, 36–53 *passim*.

31. Scammonden Dam

HEW 215

SE 053 168

Scammonden is the first, and so far the only, reservoir embankment in Britain to carry a motorway, having been designed and built as a combined water supply and highway structure. The level of the M62 as it crosses the dam is 207 ft above the original valley floor, the crest is 180 ft wide and the base of the embankment 1430 ft wide. The length of the motorway carried on the embankment is 2050 ft.

The dam is of rockfill construction with a wide internal rolled clay core, having graded sandstone fill on its upstream and downstream sides to provide for dissipation of pore-water pressure during construction and for the containment of the core. 933 000 cubic yards of overburden had to be excavated from above the foundation which, at the centre, was 42 ft below ground level. To restrict the flow of water below foundation level curtain grouting was undertaken. The volume of the embankment is 4 700 000 cubic yards.

In addition to the direct catchment, the reservoir also impounds water from an indirect catchment three times the former's area. The overflow takes the form of a bell-mouth, and the lip of the drop-shaft overflow, alongside the prominent valve shaft superstructure, is more than 32 ft below the top of the embankment and 13 ft below

Scammonden
Dam

J.A. CARTER

the floor of an access underpass through the bank; it discharges through a tunnel in the valley side. The reservoir's maximum water depth is 170 ft. Normal draw-off is through a tunnel 2750 yards long driven southwards into the adjoining valley so as to achieve the shortest route to Huddersfield; its entrance within the reservoir basin is 26 ft below topwater level. When the water level falls below the tunnel entrance, a pumping station downstream of the embankment delivers water through a rising main into the tunnel, discharging into the next valley.

Co-operation between James Anthony Gaffney, County Engineer to the West Riding County Council, and W.M. Jollans, Engineer to Huddersfield Corporation Waterworks, resulted in Herbert Lapworth and Partners being appointed as consultants. Under Peter Burgess Mitchell, the partner in charge, the reservoir was built by Sir Alfred McAlpine and Sons and was opened by the Queen on 14 October 1971.

Source

WINDER A.J.H. Scammonden Valley Scheme. *Water and Water Engineering*, 1969, **73**, 91–102.

32. Huddersfield Canal

In the Pennines, to the north of Woodhead and southwest of Huddersfield, the more practicable routes between West Yorkshire and Manchester are blocked by the high ground of Standedge. In the canal era there was competition to close the gap, resulting in three possible solutions: the long route to the north, the Leeds and Liverpool Canal, established in 1770; the middle route, extending the Aire and Calder Navigation via the Calder and Hebble by the Rochdale Canal, established in 1794; and the direct route linking Sir John Ramsden's canal at Huddersfield with the Ashton Canal above Manchester, the 20 mile long Huddersfield Canal.

The Act for the formation of the Huddersfield Canal was passed in 1794; it was to provide for boats up to 70 ft long and 7 ft wide. The first engineer approached was William Jessop, but when he declined the position, Benjamin Outram was appointed, with Nicholas Brown as surveyor. Work began almost immediately and the con-

HEW 2037

SE 145 165 to
SJ 945 990

M.F. BARBEY

Standedge
Tunnel,
Huddersfield
Canal

HEW 12

SE 007 082 to
039 118

HEW 543

SE 015 129

struction of the canal proceeded under Brown's supervision, Outram having withdrawn in 1801.

The major work on the canal was the Standedge Tunnel. Over 5456 yards long and at an elevation of some 650 ft above sea level, it was both the longest and highest of any canal in the United Kingdom. It lies on a 4 mile level and there is a 355 ft fall, with 32 locks, to the west and a 436 ft fall, with 42 locks, to the east. Many shafts were sunk during construction, some to control groundwater in the upper levels, and the tunnel was formed to a width of 9 ft and a height of 17 ft; there was a water depth of 8 ft. Such were the problems encountered during driving that the tunnel absorbed approximately one-third of the total cost of the canal.

To supply the canal with water, powers were obtained for the construction of reservoirs with a total storage capacity of some 600 million gallons, but in the event only two of those proposed were built, March Haigh, of 71 million gallons, and Slaithwaite, of 68 million gallons. The reservoirs were of traditional design, earth embankments with puddle clay cores. It was several years before March Haigh was built; its embankment was 912 ft long and 60 ft high.

Following Jessop's resignation, the advice of Thomas Telford was sought. It would seem that he was somewhat critical of the lack of water storage, suggesting in 1807 that further reservoirs should be built. The final cost of the canal was approximately £400 000 and, after its 16 year period of construction, it was finally opened on 4 April 1811, seven years after Jessop's Rochdale Canal, for which the Act was also passed in 1794.

Sources

SCHOFIELD R.B. Benjamin Outram (1764–1805), canal engineer extraordinary. *Proc. Instn Civ. Engrs*, 1979, **66**, 539–555.

SCHOFIELD R.B. The construction of the Huddersfield Narrow Canal, 1794–1811. *Trans. Newcomen Soc.*, 1981–82, **53**, 17–38.

33. Standedge Railway Tunnels

The tunnel built by the Huddersfield Canal Company proved of great value when the Huddersfield and Manchester Railway came to construct a link between the two towns. The first rail tunnel was built by Thomas Nicholson under the direction of Alfred Stanistreet Jee and, like the canal tunnel, was more than 3 miles in length. It was driven between 1846 and 1849 and was followed by a further single bore between 1868 and 1870, the engineer in this instance being William Baker and the contractor Thomas Nelson of Carlisle. Both tunnels were 15 ft wide.

HEW 1032

SE 007 082 to 039 118

The last of the Standedge tunnels was that built by the London and North Western Railway, successor to the H & MR, to supplement the two earlier single bores; it was built to a width of 27 ft and, like the others, was brick-lined. The tunnel was initially constructed by the L & NWR but, when almost complete, it was handed over to sub-contractors Williams, Lees and Thomas. Begun in 1890, it was completed in 1894. The two smaller rail tunnels lie to the south of the canal tunnel, but the latest one is to the north, necessitating an extension of the canal tunnel at its western end. None of the rail tunnels has vertical shafts; twelve side passages connect them with the canal tunnel, providing access, ventilation and drainage. The passages were also used to dispose of spoil during construction, with final removal by canal boats.

Sources

MARSHALL J. Standedge tunnel, 9 December 1967. *Stephenson Locomotive Society*, 1968, **44**, 38–42.

BLOWER A. *British railway tunnels*. Ian Allan, London, 1964, 24–27.

34. Norfolk Bridge, Sheffield

HEW 229

SK 373 892

This elegant cast iron arch forms part of the 48-span Attercliffe viaduct, 573 yards long, which carries the main line of the former Midland Railway over the valley of the River Don, just north of Sheffield Midland Station. It was built in 1868–70, late in the era of cast iron, with a span of 60 ft square, or 80 ft 7½ in. skew; it consists of six ribs, each of three segments, with a 10 ft rise of arch tapering from 2 ft 6 in. to 2 ft 3 in. deep, surmounted by N-type spandrel bracing and a 7 in. timber deck.

35. Wicker Arches, Sheffield

HEW 498

SK 359 881

The Manchester Sheffield and Lincolnshire Railway was opened to the outskirts of Sheffield in 1845 and extended over the Don valley four years later. It included a crossing of one of Sheffield's thoroughfares, the Wicker.

Much of the viaduct is now hidden by buildings, giving the impression that the Wicker arches comprise one main arch flanked by two small ones. As built, however, this was merely the main feature in a 41-arch viaduct. It was built by Miller, Blackie and Shortridge to the

Wicker Arches,
Sheffield

JA CARTER

requirements of (Sir) John Fowler, the engineer. In view of the important urban location, the detailed design was very properly entrusted to a firm of architects, Weightman, Hadfield and Goldie, and the result is rather splendid. A 72 ft span four-centred arch provides 30 ft headroom; the voussoirs continue upwards across the spandrels to the horizontal moulded course. The 12 ft span side arches are semicircular, much lower and surmounted by heraldic decoration. The whole is framed in a rectangular portal and built in good quality ashlar.

Source

Dow G. *Great Central.* Locomotive Publishing, London, 1959, 1, 131, 136.

36. Langsett Dam

The 1156 ft long embankment dam of Langsett reservoir, built between 1897 and 1904, exemplifies the state of the art of earth dam building, being thoughtfully detailed, amply dimensioned and soundly constructed. Sheffield Corporation designed and built it under the Works Engineer, William Watts, construction being by direct labour.

HEW 2035

SE 214 003

The embankment is of conventional composition, including a central puddle clay core above a concrete-filled cut-off trench which averaged 91 ft in depth. It had to be extended by a 460 ft long wing trench at the northern end and contains in total 43 000 cubic yards of concrete. The embankment itself stands 117 ft high and contains 833 000 cubic yards of material, including 69 500 cubic yards of puddle clay in the core.

The tunnel, which contains the delivery pipelines and is available to carry discharged water, passes beneath the northern end of the dam and is unusually large, 66 sq. ft in section area. The valve house which stands above it has the splendid 'waterworks baronial' appearance of that era; the shaft beneath is not only of larger diameter, 12 ft, than had hitherto been usual, but to help with illumination it is lined with white glazed bricks. The valves themselves, at three water depths, are operated by hydraulic cylinders with small feed ports to give slow movement of the valve gates. The ashlar overflow weir, at right angles to the line of the dam, is 200 ft long and, on the other side of the two-arched bridge, the spillway channel contains a series of curved steps which concentrate the flow in the centre of the channel.

The reservoir is now within the Peak District National Park. There is a display of construction photographs in the visitor centre at the north end of the dam.

Source

The Sheffield District. *Engineer*, 1904, **98**, July–Dec., 405.

37. Winscar Dam

HEW 2036

SE 154 025

Winscar Dam, built between 1972 and 1975, was the first in Britain to have an upstream face membrane of asphaltic concrete; it is 120 mm (4.8 in.) thick and was formed in two layers. The use of rock fill for the embankment itself allowed steep faces to be used and thus enabled so high a dam to be fitted onto the site between an existing earth dam and, on the downstream side, Dunford Bridge village.

The dam stands 53 m (174 ft) high, is 520 m (1706 ft) long and contains 900 000 cubic metres (1 180 000 cubic yards) of rock fill ranging in size from 1200 mm down to 2 mm. There is no valve tower in the reservoir, nor valve house on or near the dam; water is drawn at four points into the pipework in a longitudinal gallery near the upstream toe, continuing through a reinforced concrete culvert under the rock bank. The kinetic energy of water falling down the overflow chute in the eastern mitre is dissipated in a hydraulic jump pool at the foot, an innovation at an English dam.

The dam was built for the Mid Calder Water Board, based in Dewsbury, by Gleeson Civil Engineering Ltd and was designed by consulting engineers Mander, Raikes and Marshall, whose panel engineer in charge was John D. Humphreys. It is situated on the headwaters of the River Don, and in the Peak District National Park, and the area it was built to supply is in the Calder valley, some 12 miles to the north. Such inter-valley transport of water is quite common in Yorkshire.

Source

COLLINS, P.G.M. and HUMPHREYS, J.D. Winscar Reservoir, *J. Inst. Water Engrs*, 1974, **28**, 1 Feb., 17–46.

38. Woodhead Tunnels

The Sheffield, Ashton-under-Lyne and Manchester Railway was incorporated by Act of Parliament in May 1837 and six months later the construction of the Woodhead Tunnel began. The engineer was initially Charles Vignoles but he was soon superseded by Joseph Locke, whose first move was to double the estimate first made by Vignoles for the driving of the tunnel, which lies at a maximum elevation of 960 ft, falling by 80 ft to the west portal. Its average cover is 450 ft but, at one point, its floor is 600 ft below ground level.

HEW 235

SK 114 999 to
SE 157 023

The tunnel was driven from five 8 ft diameter shafts as well as from the two ends, a total of twelve faces. Although severe problems were encountered as a result of water, the tunnel was opened in December 1845, at which time it was the world's longest, at fractionally over 3 miles. Excavation had totalled 272 685 cubic yards and it had cost approximately £200 000, more than twice the original estimate. The eastern end was driven by Thomas Nicholson and the western by Richard Hattersley.

A second tunnel was built between 1847 and 1852, its contractor G.C. Pauling. Its construction proved easier than the first drive, perhaps because of the fact that, in anticipation of duplication, 25 side-access connections had been provided when the first tunnel had been built.

The earlier tunnels, both single line worked, were superseded by a double-track tunnel built between 1949 and 1953 for overhead electrification of the line, but all three are now disused so far as railway traffic is concerned.

Sources

BEAVER P. *A history of tunnels*. Peter Davies, London, 1992, 55–580.

SANDSTROM G.E. *The history of tunnelling*. Barrie and Rockliff, London, 1963, 88–89.

SCOTT P.A. and CAMPBELL J.I. Woodhead new tunnel. *Proc. Instn Civ. Engrs*, 1954, **3**, 1, 506–563.

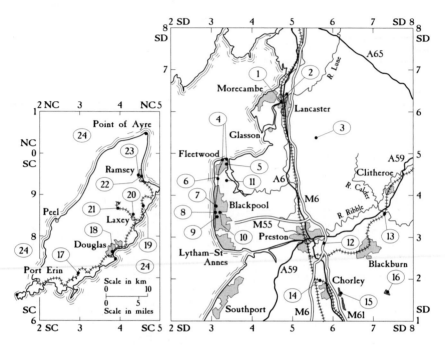

1   Skerton Bridge, Lancaster
2   Lancaster Canal
3   Abbeystead Dam
4   Fleetwood Lighthouses
5   Fleetwood Docks
6   Blackpool to Fleetwood Tramway
7   Blackpool Colonnades
8   North Pier, Blackpool
9   Blackpool Tower
10 Talbot Road Car Park, Blackpool
11 Marsh Mill, Thornton
12 Preston Bypass

13 Whalley Viaduct
14 Flying Arches, Chorley
15 Rivington Reservoirs
16 Entwistle Dam
17 Isle of Man Railway
18 Douglas Bay Tramway
19 Manx Electric Railway
20 Laxey Wheel
21 Snaefell Mountain Railway
22 Queens Pier, Ramsey
23 Ramsey Harbour Swing Bridge
24 Isle of Man Lighthouses

7. Lancashire and the Isle of Man

L ancashire is very varied in terrain, from moorland in the east to
rolling coastal plain in the west. The
county is predominantly agricultural, with the manufacturing industries mainly concentrated in
towns like Burnley along the river
valleys in the south-east. Lancaster
itself is a relatively small and quiet
city set in very pleasant surroundings.

John Frederic La Trobe Bateman (1810–89)

The coastal plain called the
Fylde is best known for its seaside
holiday resorts. Blackpool is Europe's busiest seaside holiday resort, and
its Tower is probably the best known item in this book. The Isle of Man is
also a popular holiday area, and is included in this section for that reason.

Perhaps surprisingly, these holiday areas possess many interesting
historical engineering works. The 'pursuit of happiness', as enshrined in
the American Declaration of Independence, has taxed the minds of many
British engineers, and the fruits of some of their labours are described in
this section.

Lancashire has always lain on one of the nation's principal routes of
communication from Scotland and the Lake District in the north to the
Midlands and southern England. The north–south route was established
during the Stone Age, when roughly hewn stone axes from 'factories' in
the Lake District were transported for trading further south. The route
was adapted by the Roman army for communication between the legion-
ary fortress at Chester and the headquarters of the Hadrian's Wall garrison
at Carlisle. The Roman roads later became turnpikes, and now form the
A6. The Lancaster Canal came next, following the general route in a
meandering fashion to suit the terrain; then the railways took a more direct
route, closely followed by the modern M6 motorway.

205

1. Skerton Bridge, Lancaster

HEW 754

SD 479 624

This classical structure was designed by Thomas Harrison of Chester and was completed in 1788. It carried the main road to Carlisle over the River Lune on five masonry arches, each spanning over 60 ft. The level deck of the bridge is 33 ft wide between the parapets, and there are apertures over each pier. An additional span was later built on the southern side over a railway line, though this later span is not in harmony with the rest of the structure.

2. Lancaster Canal

HEW 395

SD 529 923 to 608 068

By the late 18th century industrial developments in the north-west of England created a great demand for better access from Lancaster to Preston, Manchester and Liverpool. A canal was proposed which would enable much-needed coal from the Lancashire pits to be taken north, with agricultural produce for the industrial populace returning.

Following a survey by John Rennie, an Act was passed in 1792 authorizing a canal from Kendal to Westhoughton, near Wigan. The route chosen included only eight locks, at Tewitfield (SD 520 736), although several large aqueducts, including that over the Lune, were envisaged. It was intended that the River Ribble should also be crossed by an aqueduct, but lack of funds precluded

HEW 1349

SD 562 286

this and a tramway was constructed instead, crossing the river on a timber trestle bridge and running as far as Walton Summit (SD 582 246), whence the canal would continue to Westhoughton. The first section of the canal, from Preston to Tewitfield, was completed in 1797, followed in 1799 by the tramway and the canal from Walton Summit to Haigh (SD 810 066), where it joined the western section of the Leeds and Liverpool Canal close to Wigan top lock. At this time the eastern section of the Leeds and Liverpool had reached Burnley, and it was extended by 1810 as far as Blackburn. It was then agreed that the Leeds and Liverpool should have the use of the Lancaster south of Johnson's Hillock (SD 591 207), where the two canals finally joined in 1816. In 1859, the tramway section was closed and five years later the southern sec-

R.W. RENNISON

tion of the canal was let in perpetuity to the Leeds and Liverpool company.

Lune Aqueduct, Lancaster Canal

The canal from Tewitfield to Kendal was opened in 1819. It includes such structures as Tewitfield Locks, raising the canal 76 ft, Sedgwick Aqueduct, and Hincaster Tunnel. These structures still exist, but the construction of the M6 motorway resulted in the closure of this section in 1968. Similarly the construction of the M61 caused the closure in the same year of what had become a branch between Walton Summit and Johnson's Hillock.

A branch from Lancaster to Glasson 3 miles long with six locks was authorized in 1793 to give access to the sea; it was constructed between 1823 and 1826. The main source of the canal's water is Killington Reservoir, completed in 1819. Its embankment has been raised twice since it was built.

HEW 2049

SD 580 907

The Lune Aqueduct is the centrepiece of the Lancaster Canal. Architecturally it is the most outstanding aqueduct in north-west England, carrying the canal over the River Lune on five semicircular arches, each of 70 ft span. The whole structure is over 600 ft long. The abutments are flanked by curved wings and the structure is faced

HEW 187

SD 484 638

with rusticated masonry and topped by a stone balustrade. Work on its construction started in 1794.

Pozzolana was imported from Italy for building the concrete foundations in the piers and the construction gangs worked double shifts to complete the foundations before winter set in. As a result, construction of the aqueduct was completed in 1796.

Initially, John Rennie was appointed Engineer for the whole of the work, with William Crossley as his assistant. During the course of the work, others took over, including Henry Eastburn, Thomas Fletcher and William Cartwright on the canal and Archibald Millar on the Lune Aqueduct, with Crossley taking overall charge.

Contractors involved were John Pinkerton and John Murray for the section north of the Ribble, Paul Vickers for the southern section and Alexander Stevens for the Lune Aqueduct.

Sources

HADFIELD C. and BIDDLE G. *The canals of North West England*. David and Charles, Newton Abbot, 1970, 154, 182–211, 417–427.

CLARKE M. *The Leeds and Liverpool Canal*. Carnegie Press, 1994, 90–98, 104–105, 112–119, 254–255.

3. Abbeystead Dam

HEW 548

SD 556 538

This is an elegant stone-faced dam with an impressive curved overflow weir and spillway, built between 1878 and 1881 by Lancaster Corporation to provide a compensation water reservoir in consideration for water abstractions further upstream in the River Wyre catchment. The reservoir's capacity was originally 185 million gallons, but it is now completely silted up and the overflow acts merely as a weir on the river. The dam is 45 ft high.

It was built immediately downstream of a smaller dam of dubious stability which had been built in 1853 and raised in 1865. Between the masonry faces the dam is formed of concrete and this is believed to have been the first use of concrete in Britain to build a substantial dam. It was designed by James Mansergh, a native of Lancaster, who was subsequently engineer for Birmingham's Elan Valley Reservoirs; construction was undertaken by J. E. Hannah.

N. HOYLE

There is no public access on the dam, but a public footpath crosses the river a little way downstream.

Abbeystead Dam

Source

MANSERGH, J. M. Lancaster Waterworks Extension. *Min. Proc. Instn Civ. Engrs*, 1881–82, **68**, 253–277.

4. Fleetwood Lighthouses

Two onshore lighthouses and an offshore beacon guide ships up the channel of the River Wyre to Fleetwood. They were designed by the architect Decimus Burton and Captain Henry Mangles Denham. The offshore beacon, the Wyre Light, was on a sandbar some 2 miles offshore (SD 325 512), exposed at low tide. The light stood on a platform founded on 3 ft diameter malleable iron screwed piles installed by Mitchell and Son of Belfast, the first time their new piling system was used. It was first lit on 6 June 1840; it has now been replaced by a light buoy.

The two shore lighthouses were first lit on 1 December 1840, originally by gas but now by electricity. The ornate Beach Lighthouse, or Low Light, is three tiered, with square colonnaded base, square shaft, and octagonal top

HEW 249

SD 339 484 and SD 338 486

P. DUNKERLEY

Left: Beach Lighthouse
Right: Pharos Lighthouse

44 ft above the half-tide level, while the slender Pharos Lighthouse or High Light is 104 ft above the half-tide level. The offshore beacon platform is carried on seven timber posts, and the shore lighthouses are both built in finely worked sandstone. The lighthouses were built as part of the development of the new town and port of Fleetwood by the Preston and Wyre Railway.

Sources

DENHAM H. M. *Sailing directions from Port Lynas to Liverpool: supplement on Wyre to Port Fleetwood.* J. & J. Mawdsley, Liverpool, 1840.

MITCHELL A. On submarine foundations; particularly the screw pile and moorings. *Min. Proc. Instn Civ. Engrs,* 1848, **7**, 108–146.

5. Fleetwood Docks

HEW 832

**SD 336 472 and
SD 334 469**

The town of Fleetwood was founded in 1836 by the Preston and Wyre Railway, whose Chairman was Sir Peter Hesketh Fleetwood. The River Wyre was dredged in 1840 to provide deeper access to wharves for steamers to Scotland, Ireland and the Isle of Man. The 10 acre enclosed Wyre Dock was designed by Colonel George Landmann and was constructed for commercial traffic in

1873–77. It led to a timber pond, which was converted to the Fish Dock in 1906–08.

The decline in general cargo after World War II and the loss of the Fleetwood deep sea trawling fleet following the 'Cod War' of the 1970s led to the movement of shipping away from the enclosed docks to the riverside wharves, where an intensive roll on/roll off service to and from Ireland came into operation in 1975. The Wyre Dock has recently been converted into a very fine yachting marina, and its surrounding dock buildings have been demolished to make way for new residential, leisure and retail developments, though the inshore fishing fleet stlll operates from the Fish Dock.

Source

MARSHALL J. *The Lancashire and Yorkshire Railway.* David and Charles, Newton Abbot, 1969, **1**, 83–95.

6. Blackpool to Fleetwood Tramway

Horse trams were introduced into the United Kingdom in 1860 and steam-hauled trams in the late 1870s. In September 1885 the first electric tramway in Britain was opened on Blackpool Promenade. The 2 mile stretch was built by the Blackpool Electric Tramway Co. Ltd in co-operation with the Blackpool Corporation, which took over the ownership of the tramway in 1892. Power was supplied through an underground electrical conduit system, the installation of which was supervised by its inventor, Michael Holroyd Smith.[1] In 1898 the Blackpool and Fleetwood Tramway Co. Ltd opened a line from Blackpool North Station to the Ferry Terminal in Fleetwood. This new line used overhead electrification, and Blackpool Corporation was quick to see the advantages of this system and converted its line to the new system by the end of the following year. Various other lines were opened, and by 1920 the Corporation was sole owner of them all.[2] In 1936 the gradual closure began of all except one of the tramway routes, and the route to Marton, which closed in 1962, was the last all-street tramway in Britain. The remaining 25 track miles run from Starr Gate at the southern end of Blackpool, 11 miles north to the Ferry Terminal at Fleetwood, combining both of the for-

HEW 631

SD 305 318 to 340 484

merly separate routes. This 4 ft 8½ in. gauge tramway was for several years the only electric tramway still in operation in mainland Britain, and it maintains a year-round service as well as a tourist service in the summer.

Two of the early vehicles are preserved at the National Tramway Museum, Crich, Derbyshire.

Sources

1. SMITH M.H. The Blackpool electric tramway. *Electrician,* 1886, **17**, Sept., 370–378.

2. PHILLIPS D.F. The Blackpool and Fleetwood Tramway Co., 1896–1920. *Tramway Rev.,* 1958, **4**, 25, 2–24.

7. Princess Parade and Middle Walk Colonnades, Blackpool

Blackpool is not perhaps the first place one would look to see structures which show developments in concrete construction technology. However, there are various examples within a comparatively small area, from the 1902–11 basalt-faced mass concrete sea walls in the centre of the resort, along the 1895–99 concrete and granite 'North Shore Works', which were reconstructed in 1981–82 using reinforced concrete, to the concrete sea walls constructed between 1917 and 1937 along the extremities of the Blackpool sea front.

HEW 1258

SD 305 365

Very close to North Pier is the attractive curved Princess Parade Colonnade, constructed around the Metropole Hotel in 1912. The original blueprints, signed by the Borough Surveyor, John Shanks Brodie, reveal that the structure was constructed in small precast concrete elements reinforced in the Hennebique manner, i.e. with twisted square section main steel bars and flat hoop stirrups, unlike modern reinforcement, which is round or ribbed section steel bars. The precast columns were founded on square concrete pads, the inside edges of which rested on old 1868–70 sloping coastal defences called 'hulkings'. These were buried in 1910–11 by the construction of Princess Parade, opened by HRH The Princess Louise on 2 May 1912. The colonnade was built by J. Parkinson & Sons Ltd, and cost some £2200. Differential settlement of the foundation pads caused cracking in the columns, which had to be replaced in the 1980s.

BLACKPOOL BOROUGH COUNCIL

Further north are the impressive Middle Walk Colonnades, which are far greater in scale. The use of small precast concrete elements was repeated here for the five 82 ft long segmental bays, but the connecting straight 580 ft long covered walkways are of a much more sophisticated cantilever design, the dropped fascia beams being included for visual effect only. The overall length of these structures is some 2800 ft, and there is another small but similar segmental colonnade on Lower Walk at Gynn Square at the northern end. The Middle Walk Colonnades were designed by Blackpool Corporation and constructed in 1923–25 under the supervision of the Borough Surveyor, Francis Wood, who was also responsible for protecting the faces of the earth cliffs north of Gynn Square with rendered rubble known as 'Francis Wood's concrete outcrops'.

Middle Walk Colonnades, Blackpool

HEW 1259

SD 306 386 to 306 379

8. North Pier, Blackpool

Blackpool has three piers. This one is the earliest, and the best in the present context. It was designed by Eugenius Birch, the foremost of Victorian pier designers, built by Laidlaw and Sons of Glasgow, and opened in 1863. The 1070 ft long promenade deck is 28 ft wide, and is sup-

HEW 646

SD 305 364

213

ported on plate girders spanning 60 ft between clusters of cast iron columns founded on cast iron screw piles. A 474 ft long jetty for steamers was added in 1867, and the pier head was enlarged for a pavilion, which was opened in 1877. Other alterations have been made since then, and an estimated 12 000 tons of metal were used in its construction. Recent additions are a pier tramway along the main promenade deck and a helipad on the jetty. Central Pier, with its unconventional bowed wrought iron plate main girders, was completed in 1868. South Pier, founded on jetted piles, was built in 1893.

HEW 1006

SD 305 354

HEW 1005

SD 304 337

Source

BLACKPOOL PIER CO. LTD. *The North Pier, Blackpool, 1863–1913*. Falkner, Manchester, 1913.

9. Blackpool Tower

HEW 245

SD 306 360

Blackpool Tower took three years to build, and was opened in May 1894. The observation platform at the top is 480 ft above its base, and the height to the top of the flagstaff is 518 ft 9 in. A total of 2493 tons of steel and 93 tons of cast iron form the structure of the Tower, which dwarfs the buildings below; they contain a circus, ballroom, aquarium and other tourist attractions. The Tower was built in imitation of the Eiffel Tower, opened in Paris in 1889, and soon proved a popular attraction, despite the fact that it is so much smaller. It was designed by R.J.G. Reade, the engineer, and Maxwell and Tuke, the architects. Heenan and Froude, assisted by James Bell and R. Neill and Co. were the contractors.

Source

Blackpool Tower. *Engineering*, 1895, **59**, 575, 660–662, 727–729, 786–791.

10. Talbot Road Multi-Storey Car Park and Bus Station, Blackpool

HEW 1283

SD 310 365

Multi-storey car parks are now such a part of modern life that it may come as a surprise that the first true multi-storey car park in this country was completed in late 1939, being immediately requisitioned by the Air Ministry. It was designed by G.W. Stead of Blackpool Corporation,

Blackpool Tower

and was constructed by Atherton Bros. (Blackpool) Ltd in 1937–39. The municipal bus station comprises the ground floor, which is high enough to take double-decker buses, and the upper four main and mezzanine floors and the roof, which accommodate approximately 750 cars with 144 square feet of parking space per car. The building has a steel and concrete frame, and was extended during later years by the addition of sloping floors on its western side.

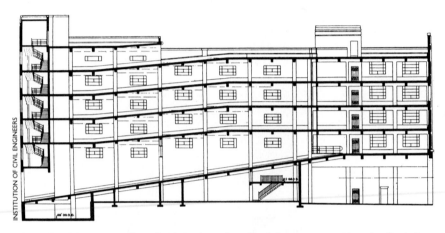

INSTITUTION OF CIVIL ENGINEERS

Talbot Road Car Park, Blackpool

One interesting detail of its construction is that the then Borough Surveyor, James Drake, was obliged to obtain his Committee's approval for the additional cost of vibrating the concrete—now a standard construction practice—to form the 18 in. thick walls of the basement, which houses public conveniences. Apart from the 1 in 7.5 gradient of the entry/exit ramp, the maximum 1 in 10 gradients of the circular spiral ramps make this multi-storey car park easier to use than many modern structures of this type.

Source

DRAKE J. Municipal works of Blackpool. *66th Annual Meeting of the Institution of Municipal and County Engineers*, Blackpool, 1939, Paper no. 1, 34–37.

11. Marsh Mill, Thornton

HEW 617

SD 335 426

The strong breezes common around Blackpool and the Fylde encouraged the use of windmills. Several survive, and the mill at Thornton is the finest in north-west England. This six-storey brick tower windmill was built in 1794 by Ralph Slater, the best known of the Fylde millwrights. It shows clearly the three distinctive features of

Fylde tower windmills: exceptional breadth in proportion to its height; tarred wooden 'cap' in the shape of an up-turned boat; and 'well frame', or 'cap centring', slung beneath the shear beams of the cap to prevent lateral movement of the cap relative to the tower. As originally built, the mill had a Lees Flyer fantail and common sails, though the sails were replaced with Cubitt's patent sails during the last century. The modern replacement sails are built on the basic framework for the patent variety.

The mill retains all its original massive wooden machinery, together with several different types of iron governors for the millstones. One of the stones is governed using Mead's automatic tentering gear, which was invented seven years before the mill was built. The mill was still in operation during the 1920s, and restoration work, started in 1965, has returned the mill to its original working order. Marsh Mill is one of only two fully preserved Fylde windmills in an area that was once nicknamed 'windmill land'. It is open to the public, and is a popular tourist attraction. The other fully preserved **HEW 769** Fylde tower mill is Lytham Mill, which was restored using machinery taken out of Little Marton Mill, Blackpool. **SD 371 270 and SD 349 341**

Source

BUTLER R.B. *et al.* A history of the Marsh Mill, Thornton: measured study. *Architecture North West*, 1964, **4**, 87–90.

12. Preston Bypass

The Preston Bypass, now part of the M6 motorway between Junction 29 (Bamber Bridge) and Junction 32 (Broughton), was the first length of motorway to be built in this country. A four-lane motorway to the north-west of England was advocated as early as 1924, but the scheme was killed by opposition from the railways. Statutory provision for the construction of motorways was not made until the passage of the Special Roads Act, 1949. **HEW 1445**

SD 567 249 to 529 341

Following the fixing of the centre-line of the $8\frac{1}{4}$ mile motorway, Tarmac Ltd began construction in June 1956. The official opening by the Prime Minister, Harold Macmillan, was on 5 December 1958.

LANCASHIRE COUNTY COUNCIL

Preston Bypass

Despite strenuous opposition from the Lancashire County Surveyor, (Sir) James Drake, whose staff designed the new bypass, it was originally constructed only as dual two-lane motorway with hard shoulders. However, Drake insisted on constructing a wide central reservation, which was taken up in 1965–66 when the motorway was widened to dual three-lane with hard shoulders, which did not continue under overbridges. Some 30 years later the motorway has been widened to dual four-lane with continuous hard shoulders, requiring the reconstruction of the bridges.

Junction 32 at Broughton, opened in January 1965, was the first three-level interchange to be completed in this country. It connects the M6 motorway with the A6 road and, from 1975, with the M55 motorway to Blackpool.

13. Whalley Viaduct

HEW 566

SD 728 362

This is the longest and perhaps the most impressive railway viaduct in Lancashire. The 48-span brick arch viaduct was completed in 1850 to carry the Bolton, Blackburn, Clitheroe and West Yorkshire Railway over the valley of the River Calder. The structure is simple in appearance, and its only concession to decoration is on the arch nearest to the remains of Whalley Abbey, where some Gothic treatment has been used to try to harmonize with the remains of the abbey. It is a very dominant feature on the local landscape. The engineer was Terence Wolfe Flanagan.

14. Flying Arches, Chorley

These 16 masonry arches were designed by Alexander James Adie to strengthen the retaining walls of a railway cutting. They are at 16 ft 6 in. centres, span 25 ft 3 in. and have a rise of 3 ft 8 in. In their centres they consist of a single layer of 12 in. thick stones topped with stone flags to prevent weathering. They were built in 1841 to strut the retaining walls at either side of the cutting against the anticipated swelling of the clay behind the walls. The cutting is on the Bolton and Preston Railway line, which was opened in 1843, and this form of construction, although simple enough in concept, is sufficiently rare in application in permanent form to be worthy of note.

HEW 751

SD 575 194

P. DUNKERLEY

Flying Arches,
Chorley

219

Source

HOSKING W. Constructions to retain the sides of deep cuttings. *Min. Proc. Instn Civ. Engrs*, 1844, **3**, 355–374.

15. Rivington Reservoirs

HEW 2043

SD 630 124 to
615 180

The Rivington water supply source developed by Liverpool comprised seven reservoirs, of which Anglezarke, Upper Rivington and Lower Rivington form the nucleus, being the first impounding reservoirs designed by Thomas Hawksley and constructed between 1850 and 1857. Viewed from the Anglezarke car park (SD 620 161), these three have the appearance of a chain of reservoirs in one river valley with a length of nearly 4 miles. In fact they straddle three shallow valleys along the foot of the Anglezarke and Rivington moors, and their innovative layout required seven independent embankments.

The names of these embankments, with their lengths and heights, are given on the map, which also shows diagrammatically the arrangement of the reservoirs, their principal feeders, the pre-reservoir routes of streams and the locations of overflows. Each of the three reservoirs has a long embankment on its western side, spreading over a saddle or river valley.

The weirs of the overflows have been partly lowered in recent years to provide the freeboard deemed necessary in respect of reservoir safety legislation. The bridges over these overflows and the cascades downstream are fine examples of the artistry for which Hawksley became noted.

The overflow cill level of Anglezarke Reservoir is 43 ft above that of Upper and Lower Rivington, which act, in effect, as one reservoir notwithstanding the dividing Horrobin embankment. The principal feed into Anglezarke is the River Yarrow, whose original course went on through the gap now filled by Yarrow embankment, not to be confused with Yarrow Reservoir. The River Douglas originally ran to the south of Horwich embankment, but was diverted into Lower Rivington along a substantial paved channel in a deep cutting.

Hawksley was ahead of his time in providing filter beds at the foot of Horwich embankment, from where a single pipeline runs for 17 miles to service reservoirs at Prescot. The extensive slow sand filters have recently been replaced by a covered multi-stage treatment plant.

Concurrent with the construction of the three above-named reservoirs, Rake Brook and Lower Roddlesworth were created on a tributary of the River Darwen to the north, and water from them brought into Anglezarke along a 4 mile long conduit, the Goit. Upper Roddlesworth dam was completed in 1863.

The small double-ended High Bullough Reservoir was built, just prior to Liverpool's arrival, by John Frederic Bateman for the Chorley Waterworks Company and the supply main subsequently ran across the bed of An-

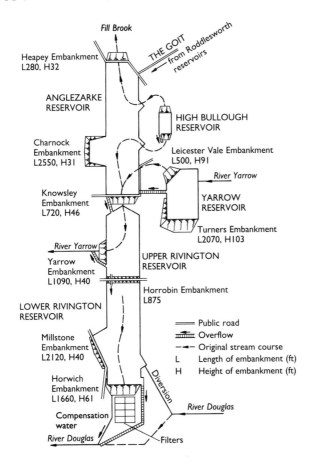

Fill Brook

THE GOIT from Roddlesworth reservoirs

Heapey Embankment
L280, H32

ANGLEZARKE
RESERVOIR

HIGH BULLOUGH
RESERVOIR

Charnock
Embankment
L2550, H31

Leicester Vale Embankment
L500, H91

River Yarrow

Knowsley
Embankment
L720, H46

YARROW
RESERVOIR

Turners Embankment
L2070, H103

River Yarrow

Yarrow
Embankment
L1090, H40

UPPER RIVINGTON
RESERVOIR

Horrobin Embankment
L875

LOWER RIVINGTON
RESERVOIR

Millstone
Embankment
L2120, H40

Horwich
Embankment
L1660, H61

Diversion

River Douglas

Public road
Overflow
Original stream course
L   Length of embankment (ft)
H   Height of embankment (ft)

Compensation
water

Filters

River Douglas

Rivington
Reservoirs

221

glezarke Reservoir. In 1856 Liverpool acquired this reservoir and took over responsibility for the water supply in Chorley.

Construction of Yarrow Reservoir was begun in 1867 to the design of Liverpool's Borough Engineer, Thomas Duncan, who died soon after work had started; activity afterwards was directed by Joseph Jackson of Bolton until the reservoir's completion in 1875. It is remarkable in comparison to its neighbours for its tall embankments. Water is discharged into Anglezarke through a tunnel beneath the west end of the Leicester Vale dam. The southern arm of Turner's embankment, which has neither discharge pipes nor overflow, stands 103 ft above original ground level but the 'puddle gutter', the cut-off trench, had to be sunk to a lowest base 257 ft below crest level.

These two embankments are formed by over a million cubic yards of built-up earthen material. Overflow water cascading 90 ft into Anglezarke Reservoir is an impressive sight; the cascade structure is anchored back into the rock ridge by steel tie rods in concrete-filled tunnels.

Sources

BINNIE G.M. *Early Victorian water engineers*. Thomas Telford, London, 1981, 136–142.

HOYLE N. *Reservoirs from Rivington to Rossendale*. North West Water Authority, Warrington, 1987, 8–15, 85–89.

16. Entwistle Dam

HEW 545

SD 723 173

In 1832 a group of mill owners obtained an Act of Parliament to become the Commissioners of the Turton and Entwistle Reservoir, to authorize 'the making and maintaining of a reservoir...for providing a more regular Supply of Water in Bradshaw Brook', and to permit the levying of a rate per foot of fall utilized by factories.

The earthen embankment forming the reservoir was duly completed in 1838 to a height of 108 ft—the first in Britain to exceed 100 ft—although, envisaging the reservoir's enlargement, land had been purchased for its height to be raised to 128 ft. Other novel features for that time were a discharge tunnel driven through the rock side of the valley, as distinct from the usual under-bank

Entwistle Dam

N. HOYLE

culvert, and a siphon draw-off. Construction was directed at first by a local surveyor, Thomas Ashworth, with some guidance from Jesse Hartley, the work being finished off and leakage cured by Joseph Jackson. With an embankment only 360 ft long, the capacity of the reservoir is 762 million gallons and its area 94 acres; as Hartley noted, the site is a favourable one for a reservoir.

This bold venture was soon overtaken by steam power and the enterprise became moribund. Relief was in prospect in 1846 when Thomas Hawksley made a bid on behalf of a proposed Lancashire Waterworks Company for the reservoir to form the basis of a venture rivalling

223

the ailing Manchester and Salford Water Company, but this prospect was stifled by Manchester Corporation deciding to establish a municipally run undertaking and develop the water resources of the Longdendale Valley.

In 1863 Bolton Corporation negotiated the purchase of Entwistle and drove a tunnel 3053 yards south-westwards from the dam, making use of Beaumont's tunneling machine, to add considerably to their water resources. As part of the deal they built Wayoh Reservoir downstream for the benefit of the mill owners.

Source

HOYLE, N. *Reservoirs from Rivington to Rossendale.* North West Water Authority, Warrington, 1987, 29–37.

17. The Isle of Man Railway

The Isle of Man is some 30 miles long by 12 miles wide. With the growth in popularity of pleasure steamers in the 1860s, the need for improved land transport for holiday traffic became apparent. It was also thought that the domestic economy could benefit from the installation of a modest railway system.

The success of the Ffestiniog Railway in Wales showed the advantages of adopting a track gauge less than the standard 4 ft 8½ in. Fair tonnages of freight and large numbers of passengers could be handled at speeds adequate for the distances involved with tremendous reductions in capital cost for curves, gradients, structures, locomotives and rolling stock.

A gauge of 3 ft was adopted and, despite many financial difficulties, a fairly comprehensive system evolved, covering a large part of the island. There is nothing exceptional in the earthworks and bridgework. The passenger stations, however, especially that at Douglas, were unusually ambitious.

HEW 834

**SC 377 753
to 197 689**

The first section, 11½ miles long, across the island from Douglas to Peel, was opened in 1873; the engineer was Henry Vignoles. The Manx Northern Railway, added in 1879, ran 16½ miles from St Johns north and north-east to Ramsey, and a 3 mile branch south from St Johns to Foxdale was added in 1886. All these have now gone.

The second line to be opened was the 15 mile Douglas to Castletown and Port Erin (south-west and west) line in 1874. This is still in use by steam passenger trains during the summer holiday season.

Source

BOYD J.I.C. *The Isle of Man Railway.* Oakwood Press, Lingfield, 1973.

18. Douglas Bay Tramway

To the layman this horse-drawn tramway is a mere tourist attraction, but it is in fact the oldest remaining horse-drawn passenger tramway in the world. It runs for nearly 2 miles along the promenade from Victoria Pier, Douglas, to Derby Castle. This 3 ft gauge line was designed and built by Thomas Lightfoot, a retired civil engineering contractor, and opened in sections between 1876 and 1902. It is operated only during the summer months.

HEW 940

SC 394 774 to 384 754

Source

PEARSON F.K. *Isle of Man tramways.* David and Charles, Newton Abbot, 1970, 21–25 and *passim*.

19. Manx Electric Railway, Isle of Man

At Derby Castle is the terminus of this railway or tramway, which uses electrically propelled bogie cars with overhead power pick-up. The track gauge is 3 ft and the 18 mile length from Douglas to Ramsey was built in three stages.

HEW 941

SC 395 774 to 452 943

The first 2½ miles opened in 1893 and in 1894 the line was extended to Laxey. The northern section to Ramsey was added in 1899 and there is a connection at Laxey to the Snaefell Mountain Railway. Taken over by the island government in 1978, it forms part of a system which has been overhauled and modernized without losing its essentially Victorian character.

20. Laxey Wheel, Isle of Man

The 'Lady Isabella' waterwheel was built in 1854 to drain the Great Laxey Lead Mine. This gigantic structure is the largest waterwheel in the British Isles, being over 72 ft in

HEW 397

SC 432 852

Laxey Wheel

diameter. It was designed by Robert Casement, a native Manxman, and its 2½ revolutions per minute produce a driving power of 200 h.p. The water that drives the wheel is trapped in a cistern further up the valley, brought to the wheel in iron pipes, lifted nearly to the top of the wheel by a syphon, and then allowed to drop onto wooden buckets attached to the wheel, thus causing it to rotate. There are 192 buckets, each capable of holding 20 gallons of water, and the total weight of the wood and iron structure is about 100 tons. The wheel used to actuate pump rods 200 yards long which ran on top of a row of 35 arches to the mine, where they operated pumps for dewatering the workings.

Source

BAWDEN T.A. *et al. The industrial archaeology of the Isle of Man.* David and Charles, Newton Abbot, 1972.

21. Snaefell Mountain Railway

This was the first electrically worked mountain railway in the British Isles, and was opened on 21 August 1895. The twin tracks rise over 1800 ft in a length of approxi-

mately 5 miles, with 85 per cent of the line being on a
gradient of 1 in 12. The running rails of Vignoles section
are secured to sleepers with fang bolts at a gauge of 3 ft
6 in. A centre rail of the type devised by John Barraclough
Fell is incorporated and is bolted to steel chairs set in the
centre of the sleepers, although it is not used for traction,
but for braking only. The route was surveyed by G. Noble
Fell, the track laid by Herd of Douglas and the electrical
equipment installed by Mather and Platt of Manchester.
Construction commenced in January 1895 and proceeded
so rapidly that the line was opened in August. The six
48-seat passenger cars use overhead pantographs designed by Edward Hopkinson. The Summit Station is
44 ft below the 2034 ft summit of Snaefell mountain, and
the bottom terminus is at Laxey.

HEW 904

**SC 433 845 to
397 879**

22. Queen's Pier, Ramsey, Isle of Man

HEW 1001

This 2150 ft long pier was built in 1882–86 at a cost of
£45 000. The contractors, Head Wrightson, probably utilized the central 3 ft gauge tramway during the construction of the pier, as they had used that expedient during
the construction of Herne Bay Pier some ten years previously.

SC 456 941

Queen's Pier is a simple structure which remains in
almost its 'as built' condition, apart from the addition of
the 1899 timber jetty. Despite its simplicity, it still has
some unconventional features, such as cruciform columns set in rows of three at 40 ft centres, the outer
columns raking, and braced by diagonal wrought iron
angles and tie rods with turnbuckles. The deck is carried
by wrought iron lattice girders, braced either side of the
columns and at mid-span by transverse lattice girders,
and the deck is also diagonally braced with wrought iron
angles. The deck construction is surprisingly complex for
such an otherwise simple pier, and comprises transverse
timbers on edge carrying tapered packing timbers to give
the deck a camber, then longitudinal timbers on flat
carrying transverse boarding. Timber string courses
carry cast iron railing standards.

Two original timber kiosks stand just inside the 1956
entrance building. The last steamer to call at the pierhead,

227

with its small refreshments room, did so in 1970. The jetty was recently partially demolished.

Sources

ADAMSON S.H. *Seaside piers.* Batsford, London, 1977, 40, 41, 102.

PEARSON F.K. *Isle of Man tramways.* David and Charles, Newton Abbot, 1970, 338–340.

23. Ramsey Harbour Swing Bridge, Isle of Man

HEW 1000

SC 452 946

This steel arch swing bridge was constructed by the Cleveland Bridge and Engineering Company of Darlington in 1892 at a cost of £2325. It is approached on its northern side by a low viaduct of eight spans, the roadway being carried on steel beams spanning between pairs of circular columns. The swinging section of the bridge covers a total length of 210 ft in two equal spans, pivoting about its centre on a circular pier of dressed masonry. The bridge is electrically operated, and carries a roadway 12 ft 6 in. wide and a footway 3 ft 6 in. wide.

Source

BAWDEN T.A. *et al. The industrial archaeology of the Isle of Man.* David and Charles, Newton Abbot, 1972, 33.

24. Isle of Man Lighthouses

HEW 833

SC 390 748

HEW 937

SC 143 640
SC 148 655
SC 149 657

There are several lighthouses of historic interest on the Isle of Man, all controlled by the Northern Lighthouse Board based in Edinburgh. That on Douglas Head is perhaps the most familiar to visitors, that on Point of Ayre at the north-east tip of the island the most accessible and those on Chicken Rock and Calf of Man, at the south-west tip, the most interesting and dramatic. The twin lights built there in 1818 by Robert Stevenson were not dissimilar in style from those at Fleetwood. They were abandoned in 1875, when the new light on Chicken Rock was brought into use, but the four-storey upper light is relatively intact. The Act for their construction was sponsored by the Member of Parliament, William Huskisson. The modern lighthouse at Calf of Man was

Point of Ayre
Lighthouse

added in 1968 and was converted to automatic operation during 1994.

Returning to Point of Ayre, the upper lighthouse was built to the design of Robert Stevenson, and was first lit on 1 February 1818. It was originally fitted with Argand lamps with a 2 ft reflector, but these were replaced by paraffin-fired lamps in 1890 by David Alan Stevenson, the grandson of the original designer. The lighthouse is now fitted with an electric light using a 250 W mercury vapour bulb running off mains power, and is visible for up to 30 miles. The iron platform around the top of the masonry tower is reached by 107 steps, and a spiral ladder with 17 rungs. The 99 ft tower carries the light 106 ft above high water level. A disused fog siren tower and a lower lighthouse stand on the foreshore a short distance away from the upper lighthouse. The lower lighthouse was rebuilt in 1950. Both lighthouses are now operated automatically.

HEW 936

NX 464 048
and NX 467 050

Source

HAGUE D.B. and CHRISTIE R. *Lighthouses*. Gomer Press, Llandysul, 1975, 101, 105, 107, 111, 112, 183–186, 220, plate 29.

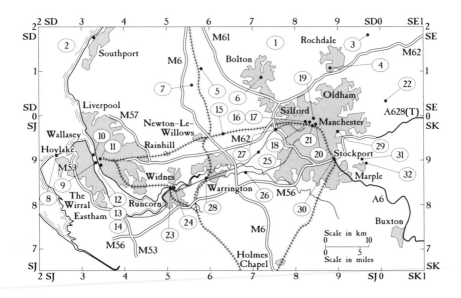

1	Thirlmere and Haweswater Aqueducts	17 Grape Street Warehouse, Manchester
2	Southport Pier	18 Deansgate Warehouse, Manchester
3	Rochdale Canal Reservoirs	19 Victoria Station, Manchester
4	March Barn Bridge, Rochdale Canal	20 Piccadilly Station, Manchester
5	Worthington Lakes	21 Manchester Central Station
6	Croal Viaduct	22 Dove Stone Reservoirs
7	Adam Bridge, near Wigan	23 Runcorn Railway Bridge
8	Wallasey Embankment	24 Runcorn–Widnes Road Bridge
9	Mersey Railway	25 Manchester Ship Canal
10	Queensway Road Tunnel	26 Bridgewater Canal
11	Royal Liver Building, Liverpool	27 Barton Aqueduct
12	Mersey Docks	28 Transporter Bridge, Warrington
13	Albert Dock, Liverpool	29 Lower Gorton Reservoir
14	Dock Swing Bridges, Liverpool	30 Stockport Viaduct
15	Liverpool and Manchester Railway	31 Brabyns Park Bridge, Marple
16	Water Street Bridge, Manchester	32 Marple Aqueduct

8. Merseyside and Greater Manchester

The short-lived metropolitan counties of Merseyside and Greater Manchester comprise most of what used to be the industrial belt of south Lancashire, the Wirral peninsula and a corner of Cheshire. Both counties overlie in part the Lancashire coalfield, which provided fuel for the heavy industrialization of this area during the last century. Greater Manchester is a huge conurbation stretching from towns on the Pennine Moors in the east to the coastal plain in the west. It is dominated by the central industrial cities of Manchester and Salford and was famous for the cotton industry, which today scarcely exists. Merseyside is slightly different in character, though still dominated by a major city, Liverpool. Although heavily populated, the coastal plain is also agricultural, and there is pleasant countryside around Southport and on the Wirral peninsula.

Communications have played a vital part in the development of this area. From the start of the Industrial Revolution, raw materials were imported through Liverpool docks in vast quantities and distributed to mills and factories inland, mostly around the area overlying the coalfield. The finished goods, mostly textiles, were then exported via Liverpool. This huge volume of cargo traffic necessitated good communications, and it is hardly surprising that the first inter-city railway in the world was built to connect Liverpool with Manchester. Rivalry between the two cities led Manchester to build a ship canal at the end of the last century to bypass the docks at Liverpool.

George Stephenson (1781–1848)

231

1. Thirlmere and Haweswater Aqueducts

As has been noted already, Manchester Corporation created reservoirs at Thirlmere and Haweswater to augment its water supplies, these being brought into use in 1894 and 1941, respectively, since when additional supplementary works have been added. In order to convey water from these sources, two very substantial aqueducts were built between the Lake District and Manchester.

HEW 1022

NY 32 15 to SD 81 03

The Thirlmere Aqueduct, when first commissioned in 1894, ran 96 miles to terminal reservoirs, now filled in and built over, at Prestwich, 4 miles north-west of the centre of Manchester. Pipelines have since been extended to, and past, reservoirs at Heaton Park and Audenshaw to form parts of a two-pipe Manchester ring main.

The basis of the first 85 miles of the aqueduct is trenched 'cut and cover' contour conduit 7 ft wide, 7 ft high to the soffit of its arched roof and having a fall of 20 in. per mile. There are 33 separate lengths of conduit totalling 36¾ miles, 22 tunnels of similar section totalling over 14 miles and 30 multi-pipe 'siphons'. The longest tunnel is the first from Thirlmere, under Dunmail Raise, 5188 yards long. The siphons, actually pressure pipelines, have three or four pipes ranging from 40 in. to 54 in. in diameter. Initially, only one pipeline of each siphon was laid and the last pipeline of the main length of aqueduct was finished in 1928.

Each pipeline was equipped at its inlet with an equilibrium float valve responding automatically to minor flow changes, but tripping shut in the event of a high flow due to a burst pipe. Most of these valves had to be modified in the 1940s to accommodate temporary axial flow pumps which increased the aqueduct's capacity pending completion of the Haweswater Aqueduct. Some intermediate pipeline valves were also designed for automatic closing in the event of bursts, a moving paddle triggering off a pneumatic servo system to close what may well have been the forerunners of present-day tilting disc valves.

Some noteworthy structural engineering can be seen in the pipe bridges over the rivers Lune and Irwell and in a tall 'viaduct' carrying the conduit over a valley near Chorley. The capacity of the aqueduct is 48 million gallons per day, carried entirely by gravity. This masterpiece of Victorian engineering was designed and directed by George Henry Hill.

The Haweswater Aqueduct was built to perform the same function. Water from Haweswater is taken through a 5 mile long atmospheric tunnel of horseshoe section 7 ft 1 in. wide by 7 ft 6 in. high, followed by a 4 mile long contour conduit of similar section down Long Sleddale, these works being constructed concurrently with the dam. A short pressure pipeline to the Thirlmere Aqueduct allowed early use of the water from Haweswater.

HEW 2045

NY 48 13 to SD 82 05

Further south, the aqueduct consists principally of six concrete-lined tunnels of 8 ft 6 in. finished diameter totalling 31 miles, linked by four-pipe siphons, each comprising two 48 in. and two 54 in. steel pipelines with welded joints, bitumen-lined and sheathed. In addition there are a few short lengths of 'cut and cover' conduit and 96 in. diameter low pressure pipe. These tunnels were driven and the first pipelines laid between 1948 and 1955 and the final pipeline finished in 1976. In its 83 mile length to Heaton Park, the aqueduct does not deviate more than half a mile from a straight line.

Covered reservoirs of 14 and 60 million gallons capacity near Bury act as balancing reservoirs for the ring mains around Manchester, which bypass Heaton Park and Audenshaw reservoirs. They have mass concrete walls and precast pre-stressed concrete roofs; when completed in 1961, the larger one was the largest covered reservoir in Britain.

South of Long Sleddale, the capacity is 105 million gallons per day, but the first 9 miles from the reservoir are of lesser capacity and unable to carry the increased yield which followed the pumping from Ullswater. A supplementary 14 mile long aqueduct to Watchgate treatment works, north of Kendal, was built, comprising a pumping station near Haweswater dam, a tunnel near the Shap fells and a falling main to Watchgate. This is the point to which water from Windermere is also pumped and a return pipe delivers treated water into the Thirlmere Aqueduct.

The first 9 miles of aqueduct were constructed by François Cementation Ltd under the direction of Manchester's project engineer Lewis Holme Lewis. The post-1948 works were again designed by Manchester's own engineers under Alan Atkinson, Engineer and Manager. Four of the tunnels were driven and lined by Edmund Nuttall Sons & Co. (London) Ltd, who also constructed the conduits and first pipelines at the northern end. The contractors for the two other tunnels were The Cementation Co. Ltd and A. Waddington & Son Ltd. Most of the first pipelines and all of the subsequent ones were laid by Manchester's Direct Works Section. All the steel pipes were manufactured by South Durham Steel and Iron Co.

Sources

HILL G.H. The Thirlmere works for the water supply of Manchester. *Min. Proc. Instn Civ. Engrs*, 1895–96, **126**, 2–23.

HOYLE N. and SANKEY K.A. *Thirlmere Water—a hundred miles, a hundred years*. Centwrite, Bury, 1994.

2. Southport Pier

HEW 831

SD 335 176

The pier at Southport was the first seaside pier to be founded on jetted piles, a technique pioneered in France, and it was designed by (Sir) James Brunlees and built by W. and J. Galloway. When opened in 1860 it was the longest in the country, at 3600 ft, and it was subsequently extended in 1864 and 1868 to a total of 4380 ft. At the same time the pier was widened and its three rows of piles were increased to four, the new piles being jetted into the sand of the sea-bed a distance of 15 to 20 ft in an average time of about 25 minutes each. The pier carries modern amusement facilities and a narrow gauge railway, which replaced the original tramway, installed in 1863. Because of repeated storm damage the length of the pier has been reduced to its present 3650 ft.

Source

HOOPER H. Description of the pier at Southport, Lancashire. *Min. Proc. Instn Civ. Engrs*, 1861, **20**, 292–299.

Method used for
sinking the piles
of Southport
Pier, 1860

INSTITUTION OF CIVIL ENGINEERS

3. Rochdale Canal Reservoirs, High Level Group

On the bleak Pennine moorland 6 miles north-east of Rochdale are the embankments of four reservoirs built by the Rochdale Canal Company. They are, with dates of completion: Blackstone Edge (1801), White Holme (1816), Light Hazzles (1827) and Warland (1857). In 1827 the first three probably represented the greatest concentration of reservoir storage and embankment volumes in Britain and, as an indication of their size, the Pennine Way runs along more than 2 miles of these embankments, which are up to 55 ft high. The total capacity of the four reservoirs, before recent alterations, was 1018 million gallons. The first two are attributed to William Jessop.

HEW 1931

SD 970 180 to 955 215

235

White Holme in fact lies beyond the watershed, in Yorkshire, water being drawn westwards through a shallow tunnel under the bed of Light Hazzles. There are no significant feeder streams into these reservoirs, water having been collected by 18 miles of catchwater 'drains'. In 1923 these reservoirs were acquired jointly by Oldham and Rochdale Corporations, who restored some of the dilapidation and harnessed them for water supply. Further improvements have been carried out very recently to Blackstone Edge and White Holme, and Light Hazzles embankment has been cut through.

Source

BINNIE G.M. *Early dam builders in Britain*. Thomas Telford, London, 1987, 79–89.

4. March Barn Bridge, Rochdale Canal

The original survey and estimates for the Rochdale Canal were made by John Rennie, although he had little to do with the scheme after that. The final survey for the route was made by William Crossley, and the canal was designed by William Jessop, the resident engineer being Crossley, who was succeeded by Thomas Townshend. One of the contractors involved is known to have been John Gilbert.

HEW 370

SD 886 110

March Barn Bridge carries a road across the canal at a skew angle of $60°$. The bridge was completed in 1797, and the canal was opened in two sections on different dates in 1798. The most interesting feature about March Barn Bridge, apart from its skew, is that the stones forming the voussoirs of the single arch span were laid in winding courses. This difficult form of construction called for a high degree of skill on the part of the stonemasons who built the bridge; it is one of the oldest masonry skew arches in the United Kingdom.

Sources

BOUCHER, C.T.G. *John Rennie 1761–1821: the life and work of a great engineer*. Manchester University Press, Manchester, 1963.

HADFIELD, C. and SKEMPTON, A. W. *William Jessop, engineer*. David and Charles, Newton Abbot, 1979.

5. Worthington Lakes

These reservoirs originated with a water supply scheme
for the Wigan Local Board in the early 1850s. The two
main reservoirs of the four lie in the vacated valley of the
River Douglas, the river having been diverted through a
tunnel, this ingenious development being the work of
(Sir) Robert Rawlinson, at the time principally occupied
as an engineering inspector for the government's Central
Board of Health. In this capacity he 'visited, inspected
and reported upon the principal towns in England, from
Berwick upon Tweed to Penzance'[1] and produced designs for waterworks at many of them.

HEW 1432

SD 58 10

The present areas of water, from south to north, are
named Worthington, Arley, Adlington and Sylvester.
The original intention, begun in 1853, was to impound
the Adlington Brook by a forerunner of the Arley embankment, with a short side embankment to close off the
gorge and incorporate an overflow. Problems with coal
mines and their owners led to a change of plan whereby
this reservoir was truncated by the Adlington embankment, built upstream in 1861, and Arley embankment
rebuilt, thus creating an elevated reservoir within the
original river valley. Water was brought from further up
Adlington Brook by a feeder channel and the residual
flow in this stream discharged through a tunnel under
part of Arley reservoir into the Douglas. To replace some
of the lost storage, Worthington reservoir was added,
after the river diversion tunnel had been extended downstream.[2]

In due course the empty Adlington basin was partly
filled as a reservoir, so as to provide compensation water
direct to a factory by means of a pipe running through
the river tunnel, and the small Sylvester Lodge reservoir
was created by carrying a public footpath across the
valley on an embankment. The overflow level of the
Adlington reservoir, impounded by the Adlington embankment, is in fact lower than that of Arley, downstream
of it. The capacities of Worthington, Arley and Adlington
reservoirs are 114, 103 and 10 million gallons respectively, and the greatest depth of water, in Worthington,
is 42 ft.

Sources

1. RAWLINSON R. *Public works in Lancashire*. P. S. King, London, 1898, 127–129.

2. NORTH WEST WATER. *Worthington Lakes—a historical, engineering and amenity appreciation*. Civic Trust in the North West, Swinton, 1993.

6. Croal Viaduct, Bolton

HEW 251

SD 722 093

This viaduct carries a railway over a dual carriageway, a culverted river and a filled-in canal. It was designed by Charles Vignoles and built in 1847. Its four main arches are of cast iron and have a skew span of 76 ft and a rise of 13 ft. There are six ribs each in three segments. Their design is simple, with plain verticals in the spandrels and transverse bracing tie-rods and barrel struts. The other six arches of the viaduct were built as segmental stone arches, with spans of 36 ft and 12 ft rise. Two of the masonry piers have been strengthened at springing level with steel collars. The ironwork was by Ogle and Son of Preston.

Croal Viaduct

7. Adam Bridge, near Wigan

This viaduct of four spans carries the former Liverpool
and Bury Railway over the River Douglas, an occupation
road and a footpath. It was originally constructed in 1847,
and was strengthened successively in 1869, 1888 and
1906. In 1947 it was rebuilt with pre-stressed concrete
beams. The beams are 2 ft 8 in. deep, and there are six
beams to each track, with a further two beams carrying
each parapet. Although pre-stressed beams were precast
by the London, Midland and Scottish Railway in 1938–39
for use in the wartime emergency replacement of road
bridges over railways, the Adam Bridge was the first
bridge in the country to carry live railway loading on
such beams. The bridge was designed by William Kelly
Wallace, Chief Engineer of the London, Midland and
Scottish Railway, and the contract for its erection was
carried out by Leonard Fairclough Ltd.

HEW 1048

SD 572 052

Source

A prestressed concrete railway bridge near Wigan. *Concrete Construc.
Engng*, 1947, **42**, Nov., 305–308.

8. Wallasey Embankment

Birkenhead lies across the River Mersey from Liverpool
and north of Birkenhead is Wallasey which, with Bootle
opposite, marks the end of the river.

    The coastline of the Wirral between Wallasey and
Hoylake, that is between the rivers Mersey and Dee, is
low lying, particularly in the central portion. It needs
protection from the sea, not only to prevent flooding of
the hinterland, but also to protect the port of Liverpool,
which would be devastated if major erosion allowed the
Mersey to form two exit channels. Moreover, evidence
suggests that this part of the Wirral is sinking at a rate of
3 ft every 100 years.

    In 1794 a 'slope wall or pavement' was built between
Wallasey and Hoylake to reinforce the sand dunes. Made
from local sand, clay, silt and peat, it was only partially
successful. In 1829 a structure 2900 yards long, known as
the 'old embankment', was built at a cost of £32 000. Its
seaward slope varied between 1 in 4 and 1 in 8, and it was

HEW 271

**SJ 241 911 to
267 921**

faced with 2 ft of local clay, which was later armoured with sandstone blocks. The square blocks varied in size from 8 in. to 18 in. and they were laid dry in bonded courses. Continuous maintenance was necessary, and in 1894 extensions were built at either end called the 'new embankment', bringing the total length of the structure to 2¼ miles at a cost of £16 370. A toe wall to prevent undercutting was built at a later date.

In 1941 the structure was faced with concrete about 6 in. deep, the concrete being laid in a cellular pattern, the cells about 13 ft square. However, the 19th-century sandstone blocks stood up to the weather better than the 20th-century concrete, and the passage of time inevitably meant that the structure has had to have major rebuilding done to it. This rebuilding started in 1973 and was completed in 1981.

To the east of the Wallasey Embankment are several modern coastal defence structures worthy of note, all designed by the Metropolitan Borough of Wirral. These include the Leasowe Bay Offshore Breakwaters, one of them being Wallasey Offshore Breakwater, the first such structure in Britain constructed primarily for coastal defence purposes, and built in 1981. Later offshore artificial reefs near Perch Rock (SJ 309 947) are topped with precast concrete units which are submerged at high water, and there is a novel curved 'colonnade' structure around New Brighton Pumping Station (SJ 312 942), constructed of 'MERMADE' precast concrete units in 1987, to cater for waves reflected off the walls of Seaforth Dock on the opposite bank of the Mersey.

HEW 1430

SJ 265 923

Source

BELL M.N. *et al*. The Wallasey Embankment. *Proc. Instn. Civ. Engrs*, 1975, **58**, 569–590.

9. Mersey Railway

HEW 1049

SJ 351 900 to 326 375 and 307 896

Authorized by Acts of Parliament of 1871 and 1882, the Mersey Railway, designed by Sir Charles Fox & Sons, includes Britain's second oldest subaqueous railway tunnel, the earliest being the Thames Tunnel, which had begun carrying railway traffic in 1869.

The double-line running tunnel is horseshoe in shape

and is 50 ft 6 in. wide at the stations and 26 ft wide between them; it was mainly driven through faulted triassic sandstone. As steam engines were used initially, a 7 ft diameter ventilation tunnel was provided, as well as a 7 ft diameter drainage tunnel which falls from the centre of the underwater section to pumping stations at each side of the River Mersey. These two tunnels were driven by Beaumont machine. The running tunnel also falls for some 800 ft each side of the estuary to assist drainage; it then rises at gradients of 1 in 36 and 1 in 27 to Liverpool and Birkenhead.

The first stations on either side, James Street (SJ 344 903) and Hamilton Square (SJ 326 890), are deep level, reached by lifts originally worked hydraulically and using tanks housed in two of the tallest towers, 171 ft high, ever built at a British railway station. The vertical travel of the lifts is 76 ft 8 in. at James Street and 87 ft 9 in. at Hamilton Square. The three lifts at each station can each accommodate 100 passengers; they were later converted to electrical working, but the tower at Hamilton Square remains, dominating the small station building.

The contractor was Samuel Isaac, but the construction work was sublet to John Waddell & Sons and work began in 1880. The line was opened between James Street and Green Lane (SJ 326 875) in 1886, followed by the branch from Hamilton Square to Birkenhead Park (SJ 307 896) in 1888, connecting there with a branch of the Wirral Railway, opened the same day. A further extension was opened from James Street to Liverpool Central (SJ 351 900) in 1892, by which time the Mersey Railway had been connected to the Birkenhead Joint Railway.

It was found that the ventilation fans could not cope adequately with steam locomotives and so the line was electrified by British Westinghouse in 1903, using direct current. Following modification of the tunnel system between 1972 and 1977, the railway came to form part of the Merseyrail Underground.

Sources

Fox F. The Mersey railway. *Min. Proc. Instn Civ. Engrs*, 1886, **86**, 40–59.

Parkin G.W. *The Mersey railway*. Oakwood Press, Lingfield, 1965.

Biddle G. *Victorian stations*. David and Charles, Newton Abbot, 1973, 130, 155.

10. Queensway Road Tunnel

HEW 1747

SJ 347 908 to 326 886

When opened by King George V on 18 July 1934, the Queensway Road Tunnel under the River Mersey between Liverpool and Birkenhead was the largest subaqueous road tunnel in the world. The tunnel was designed by Mott, Hay and Anderson. Contractors for the river tunnel and Liverpool land tunnels were Edmund Nuttall Ltd. The Birkenhead land tunnels were constructed by Sir Robert McAlpine & Sons. The main tunnel is 10 620 ft long, and there are two branches 1654 ft and 1561 ft long. The central portion under the Mersey is 5204 ft long, is of circular cross-section with an internal diameter of 44 ft, and has a 36 ft wide carriageway. The tunnel is lined with cast iron rings. Because of increased traffic over the years, the tunnel was supplemented during the 1970s by the construction of the Kingsway Road Tunnel.

Source

Queensway Road Tunnel

ANDERSON D. The construction of the Mersey Tunnel. *J. Instn Civ. Engrs*, 1936, **2**, 473–544.

Royal Liver
Building, Liverpool

S. MULHOLLAND

11. Royal Liver Building, Liverpool

This well known building at Liverpool Pierhead was
designed by Walter Aubrey Thomas with the co-operation of L.G. Mouchel and Partners. The contractors were
William Brown and Sons of Salford for the site, which
involved filling in the George's Dock, and Edmund Nuttall and Co. of Trafford Park, Manchester, for the structure. It is not generally realized today that this is not of
traditional load-bearing masonry, but a reinforced concrete structure.

HEW 102

SJ 338 904

243

The foundation stone was laid on 11 May 1908 and the building was opened on 19 July 1911. The rapid completion of what was then thought to be the largest reinforced concrete structure in the world was attributed largely to the form of construction. It has nine main floors, two more in the roof structure and six more in the towers.

The building cost £621 000 and originally had 19 lifts, although there are now only eleven. The principal dimensions are 301 ft by 177 ft, with heights of 167 ft to the main roof, 220 ft to the clock and 322 ft to the top of the 18 ft high Liver Birds. The clock is slightly larger than Big Ben. It was set in motion at 1.40 p.m. on 22 June 1911, at the moment King George V was crowned in Westminster Abbey. At that time it was the largest electric clock in the British Empire.

Source

LAKEMAN A. The Royal Liver Building, Liverpool. *Concrete Construc. Engng*, 1911, **6**, Oct., 727–735.

12. Mersey Docks

HEW 1384

SJ 31 97 to 35 87

The development of Liverpool's dock systems has much in common with that of Hull. In both cases the mouth of a local river, joining a major waterway not far from the open sea, provided a ready made haven. Simple jetties and quays with the addition of a graving dock gave place to an enclosed dock and basin. Larger docks were added to left and right and eventually the original facilities, completely outmoded, were abandoned and filled in.

The Ler pool or 'Sea Lake' became the Old Dock about 1715, under the direction of Thomas Steers. It had an entrance basin and a small dry dock to one side, which

HEW 1582

SJ 340 900

was enlarged 15 years later and became Canning Dock. On the other side, South Dock appeared about 1750 and was later named Salthouse. The first stage in the development of the Canning Graving Docks began in 1765, when they were constructed from excavations revetted with irregular courses of masonry blocks. George's Dock and Basin followed on the north side in 1770. South of

HEW 1843

SJ 343 896

Salthouse, Duke's Dock, the virtual terminus of the Bridgewater Canal, was opened in 1773, and was followed by King's Dock about 1786 and Queen's in 1796, and then by Brunswick Dock, the first of Jesse Hartley's dock constructions in Liverpool.

On the other side, north of George's Dock, Princes, Waterloo and Clarence Docks were in use by 1839. By this time the Old Dock had been filled in and the Customs House built on the site. Meanwhile, just on the Mersey side of the Salthouse Dock, the Albert Dock and warehouses were constructed.

The Victoria Tower, with a clock on each of its six faces, was constructed by Hartley at the river entrance of Salisbury Dock in 1846–48, typically using granite. Working in collaboration with the engineer to the canal company, he built a flight of locks to connect the Liverpool dock system at Stanley Dock with the Leeds and Liverpool Canal; the commercial significance of the connection far outweighed the scope of the work, requiring four locks of traditional design, and using hand-operated gates with a variety of paddle machinery. Improved security was provided to Princes Dock in 1821 by the addition of a boundary wall. This practice was continued in 1851–52 with the construction on a much grander scale of a granite rubble masonry wall some 13 ft high along Regent Road between South Collingwood Dock and Huskisson Dock. Five of the original fortress-like gateways remain, giving controlled access to and from the docks.

The Birkenhead Docks developed from 1847 in a manner different from those across the River Mersey in Liverpool, being created by James Meadows Rendel via the walling-in and deepening of Wallasey Pool, which resulted in continuous lengths of quays with space to spare. However, limited water depths restricted the size of shipping. To improve access to the Mersey Docks, training banks were constructed in stages between 1909 and 1960, revetting the sides of the natural sandbanks in the estuary to direct the flow of the Mersey and to prevent erosion.

HEW 1546

SJ 333 921

HEW 1828

SJ 340 922

HEW 1739

SJ 336 921 to 337 931

HEW 1384

SJ 32 89 to 29 91

HEW 1656

SD 18 04 to SJ 30 95

Sources

NORFOLK R.N. Mersey estuary and approach channels. *Trans. Liverpool Nautical Research Soc.*, 1987.

JARVIS A. *Liverpool Central Docks, 1799–1905.* Alan Sutton, Stroud, 1991.

RITCHIE-NOAKES N.R. *Liverpool's historic waterfront.* HMSO, London, 1984.

13. Albert Dock and other Warehouses, Liverpool

HEW 101

SJ 341 897

The Albert Dock Warehouses were designed by Jesse Hartley and Philip Hardwick on the Mersey side of Salthouse Dock, and were opened by HRH Prince Albert in 1846. They included the first dockside fire-resistant warehouses in Liverpool, and resemble those at St Katharine's Dock, London. The concept was monumental in appearance and strength, and the complex is the largest single group of Grade I listed buildings in Great Britain.

The warehouses are constructed of brick, varying from 3 ft to 18 in. in thickness; cast iron pillars, 4 ft in diameter and 16 ft high, rise from the level of the granite quay. One pillar on the south side of the dock carries a plaque installed by the Institution of Civil Engineers to commemorate Jesse Hartley. The interior structure is in bays of 19 ft by 12 ft with slim cast iron columns carrying inverted Y-shaped cast iron beams spanning 19 ft. These take brick jack arches of 12 ft span with wrought iron tie bars. The supports are founded partly in granite over sandstone bedrock and partly on beech friction piles driven into silty sand. The first and second storeys are 12 ft high and the third and fourth storeys are 11 ft high. These warehouses comprise five 5-storey blocks, rising 60 ft to the galvanized sheet iron roof on the four sides of the 6¾ acre 650 ft by 450 ft dock; they were for 50 years used principally in the handling of cloth, tobacco, wines and spirits. After the obsolescence of this system at the turn of the century the warehouses and the vaults below the quay were used for the bonded storage only of wines, spirits and tobacco until 1970, the dock having been closed to shipping in 1946.

The warehouses were redeveloped during the 1980s into the Merseyside Maritime Museum, the Tate Gallery, television studios, shops, restaurants, tourist attractions, conference and meetings facilities and offices.

HEW 1545

SJ 336 913

The East Waterloo Grain Warehouse is the only original granary remaining at Waterloo Dock, and was constructed in 1863–68. Designed in-house by George Fosbery Lyster, the granary stored the grain on the

ground floor and five upper floors rather than in silos. The brick warehouse has ornamental masonry details, and the upper floors have cast iron columns, those on the ground floor being of brickwork. The original grain-handling hydraulic machinery had been supplied by Sir W.G. Armstrong & Co. The warehouse was refurbished as apartments in 1992–94, when the roof was slated.

Albert Dock warehouses

The North and old South Tobacco Warehouses at Stanley Dock were designed by Jesse Hartley, the northern building having been constructed by William Tomkinson in 1852–54, the southern building following a year later. They were designed to be fire resistant, in brick and iron, though the warehouses had roof coverings of board and slates. There is a colonnade of massive columns on the quayside, and the 630 ft long buildings are in five sections, each with a 38 ft embayment for cargo handling. A 15 ft high brick wall protects the bonded area. The South Warehouse was extended in 1916 with a reinforced concrete annexe on its southern side. Sections damaged during World War II were repaired in 1953.

HEW 1740

SJ 337 922 and SJ 337 920

Additional bonded tobacco storage capacity was provided at Stanley Dock in 1897–1901, when the southern part of the dock was infilled, a new dock wall was constructed, and a new warehouse was built on the re-

HEW 1741

SJ 336 922

claimed land. The South (New) Stanley Tobacco Warehouse was designed by Anthony George Lyster, and was built by Morrison & Sons, with hydraulic lifts and hoists by Easton, Anderson & Goolden Ltd and John Abbot & Co. Ltd, respectively. This is reputedly the largest tobacco warehouse in the world, being 165 ft wide, over 700 ft long, and on 14 levels, including vaults. It is connected to the older South Stanley Tobacco Warehouse by three bridges at first floor level. The columns are encased in fireclay and the ironwork of the floors is encased in concrete in order to provide greater fire protection.

Sources

GREENSLADE R. Albert Dock, Liverpool: reinstatement. *Consult. Engr*, 1976, **40**, Feb., 22–25.

PARKINSON G. and CURTIN W.C. Albert Dock, Liverpool—structural survey. *Struct. Engr*, 1986, **64A**, Oct., 283–290.

TALLIS J.A. *et al.* Restoration of Albert Dock. *Struct. Engr*, 1986, **64A**, 291–298.

14. Albert Dock and Canning Dock Swing Bridges, Liverpool

The Albert Dock cast iron bridge carries a roadway, whilst the smaller Canning Dock timber bridge carries only a footway. Both were designed by Jesse Hartley, and both have double opening leaves.

HEW 1386

SJ 340 898

The Albert Swing Bridge spans a 44 ft 9 in. wide passage with two 30 ton leaves of equal length, 46 ft 6 in., and was built in 1842–43 by the Haigh Foundry of Wigan. It has four cast iron ribs to each leaf, bolted to a turntable, the bottom plate being bolted down to the sandstone masonry of the bridge pit. The bridge has pitch pine decking with wrought iron railings, and carries two footways 3 ft 4 in. wide and a cartway 7 ft 9 in. wide, the overall width of the deck being 15 ft 8 in. The bridge was taken down and rebuilt in 1984, when some details, such as the bolting and the 4 in. thick elm horseblock paving, were replaced using more modern materials and methods.

HEW 1391

SJ 342 899

A timber swing bridge spans a 44 ft 3 in. wide passage between Canning Dock and Canning Half-tide Dock, and was built in 1846, probably by direct labour. The bridge has two leaves of unequal length, respectively 51 ft 8½ in. (south) and 40 ft 0½ in. (north) measured along the centre lines. Each leaf comprises longitudinal main tapering timbers, spaced apart by transverse scantlings, to which the pitch pine decking is spiked. This bridge was also rebuilt in 1984 with new timbers, but incorporating the original wrought iron stays.

Sources

RITCHIE-NOAKES N.R. *Jesse Hartley, Dock Engineer to the Port of Liverpool, 1824–1860*. Merseyside County Museum, 1980, 30.

HUGHES Q. *Seaport*. Lund Humphries, London, 1964, 27–30.

15. Liverpool and Manchester Railway

The Liverpool and Manchester Railway was the world's first inter-city railway. The 31 mile route crosses terrain which presented considerable difficulties to George Stephenson, whose original route was rejected by the House of Lords in 1824. A new route was surveyed by the Rennies and Charles Vignoles, and following its sanction by Parliament in 1826, Stephenson was re-engaged as engineer in charge of construction.

HEW 223

SJ 345 894 to 833 978

At Liverpool, the line terminated after tunnels which were included in cable worked inclines. The single track Crown Street Tunnel was only 291 yards long, 15 ft wide and 12 ft high, the gradient falling eastwards so that departing trains proceeded by gravity from the original passenger terminus at Crown Street to the 40 ft deep cutting at Edge Hill. The double track Wapping Tunnel was 2111 yards long, with a cross section of 22 ft by 16 ft high, running up from the docks. When opened in July 1829, the walls were whitewashed and gas lighting was installed, making the tunnel quite a tourist attraction. Locomotive working replaced the cable operations in May 1896, and lasted until 1965, when the Park Lane goods yard it served was closed and the tunnel was no longer needed.

HEW 953

SJ 345 894 to 369 893

Vignoles was in charge of construction when work started, but arguments with Stephenson forced his resignation, and Joseph Locke took over supervision. A sec-

249

HEW 1359

SJ 350 907 to 372 899

ond tunnel into Crown Street was made to a size appropriate for locomotive working. A fourth tunnel, 2220 yards long, included in a 2370 yard cable-operated incline, was built by William Mackenzie from Edge Hill to a new terminus at Lime Street in 1836. The incline was rope-worked until 1870, and the tunnel was partly opened out in the 1880s. A fifth tunnel was provided in 1849 between the present Edge Hill Station and the Victoria and Waterloo Docks, cable-worked until 1895.

The stationary-engine houses at Edge Hill cutting were linked by a monumental Moorish arch. Edge Hill possesses the oldest passenger station buildings in the world still in daily use. A goods yard was also constructed there. Lime Street Station, the present-day Liverpool terminus, was opened in August 1836. The earliest

HEW 103

SJ 351 906

roof had timber trusses on cast iron columns and arcades. This was replaced about twelve years later by an iron roof of single span 153 ft 6 in., with curved trusses over six tracks, three platforms and a roadway. In 1865–67 the whole station was lengthened towards Manchester and widened, and the first of the two existing roofs was provided, approximately 600 ft long, the width varying from 215 ft to 185 ft down the curved tapering site. A second span, tapering from 195 ft to 170 ft, was added in 1875, with both bottom and top main members of the trusses being curved with intervening bracing of the Warren girder type. The trusses are at 32 ft centres and are 44 ft 9 in. high, comprising a combination of different iron sections.

As well as the 40 ft rock cutting at Edge Hill, there was an imposing 70 ft deep cutting at Olive Mount with almost vertical rock sides. A prodigious feat of excava-

HEW 553

SJ 490 914

tion, this cutting is no longer so impressive, as it was widened subsequently. At Rainhill, a skew arch bridge carried the 1753 turnpike road, now the A57 between Liverpool and Manchester, over the railway. The bridge has a skew angle of 34° and a skew span of 54 ft—30 ft square—making the voussoirs a very odd shape. The stone was obtained from a local quarry, and the bridge cost £3735 to construct. Legend has it that, to enable the masons to select and cut the voussoirs correctly before erection, a wooden model, possibly full size, was made

S. MULHOLLAND

and cut up as necessary along the course lines. The fame of Rainhill Bridge is such that it is sometimes assumed to be unique, whereas Booth's schedule shows it to be one of 16 skew bridges on the Liverpool and Manchester Railway, such as Winton Bridge, with its 31 ft skew span, carrying the railway over a local road. Sutton Bridge has a 30 ft square span and an almost semicircular arch, with voussoirs as at Rainhill continued radially up to the horizontal string course. It carries road over rail, and is one of the best surviving of the early bridges.

Rainhill Bridge

HEW 954

SJ 760 984

HEW 945

SJ 522 926

The more direct route was intended to pass through a ridge of Triassic limestone, just east of Liverpool, in tunnels, with inclines worked by stationary engines to haul trains over a second ridge 9 miles further east. However, the Rainhill Trials of October 1829 proved that locomotive traction could be used on the inclines, thus dispensing with the need for stationary engines and cable haulage. Prior to this, the exact mode of traction had not been decided, and horse traction would have been an option. There were five entries for the Trials, and it was won by Robert Stephenson's *Rocket*, which incorporated

HEW 944

SJ 482 913 to 510 920

251

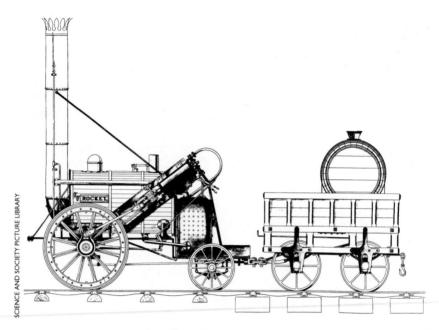

Robert
Stephenson's
Rocket

HEW 94

SJ 569 948

a multi-tube boiler. Its final run at 35 miles per hour caused a sensation.

Sankey Viaduct was the first major viaduct of the railway era, and owed something of its design to the earlier canal aqueducts. It was begun in 1828, and opened in September 1830. Its nine semicircular arches, each of 50 ft span, carry the railway over the Sankey Brook at a height of 70 ft. The brick viaduct has stone facings, and each of its piers rests on approximately 200 timber piles some 20–30 ft long. The wide splay of the pier bases gives the viaduct a particularly sturdy appearance, but the slender pilasters extending from them up to the parapets add a graceful touch.

A branch line to Warrington was authorized in 1829, engineered by Robert Stephenson, and opened in 1831. Its junction with the Liverpool and Manchester Railway was originally called Newton Junction, but from 1861 was known as Earlestown. When the Grand Junction Railway was opened from Birmingham, the branch became part of the main line from Euston to Liverpool. An east curve was added in 1837 to serve Manchester. The Vulcan Foundry, one of the famous locomotive building

HEW 946

SJ 578 951

252

firms, was located on the branch, and the London and North Western Railway set up a wagon works at Earlestown. On the island platform at Earlestown Station is a Tudor-style waiting room of some architectural merit, probably built in the early 1840s; it has an unusual and rather attractive platform awning.

Newton Viaduct is somewhat overshadowed by its more illustrious neighbour, Sankey Viaduct, but is still quite an attractive structure. The 40 ft high red brick viaduct has stone voussoirs and pilasters, and four semicircular arches of 30 ft span.

HEW 932

SJ 593 953

One of the major engineering achievements of the Liverpool and Manchester Railway was the conquest of Chat Moss, a glacial depression or basin ranging from 15 to 36 ft deep, and more than filled with waterlogged vegetable matter, its surface resembling a shallow dome. Five miles of the track ran across it. Any suggestion in 1826 to build a railway across such ground met with scepticism and ridicule, but George Stephenson was convinced that it could be done, using a technique that had been adopted before: spreading the load over a wide base using bundles of heather or 'mattresses' of brushwood. Generally, construction operations went well, apart from the eastern end, where progress even became negative during 1827. Old tar barrels were used to make wooden

HEW 952

SJ 68 97 to 73 98

Sankey Viaduct

ACKERMANN. 1831

culverts for the two side ditches 48 ft apart, and Botany Wood was purchased to supply small trees, branches and twigs for making hurdles. Dried peat, earth and cinders were eventually used and on 1 January 1830 *Rocket* was able to pass over with a trial train. In 1974, engineers building the M62 motorway were able to use mechanical plant to lay the road's foundation on a firmer underlying stratum, whereas Stephenson, who had to rely on hand digging, could not. A good impression of the conditions can be obtained by standing near to the easily accessible Astley signal box and feeling the ground tremble as a train passes.

HEW 911

SJ 829 979

The original bridge across Water Street led to what is widely regarded as the oldest railway station in the world. Completed in 1830, the original bridge was the first iron beam bridge, as distinct from an arch or truss, to carry a railway using locomotives. It made pioneer use of I-section cast iron beams with a clear span of 26 ft. There were three main beams $27\frac{1}{2}$ in. deep, with a 16 in. by 3 in. bottom flange, 4 in. by 3 in. top flange, and with smaller cross beams and brick jack arches. Fairbairn and Lillie were the contractors, and (Sir) William Fairbairn almost certainly designed the superstructure. The pre-

Water Street
Bridge

ACKERMANN, 1831

sent bridge dates from 1908, and is a very ordinary steel plate girder bridge, by comparison of modest span.

Liverpool Road Station was built on a deviation from the original route, which would have terminated at Salford. This required the construction of a stone bridge over the River Irwell with two arches of skew span 66 ft and 64 ft 6 in. square span, 53 ft wide between parapets, accommodating a double line of railway and also an 18 ft wide roadway. East of the river bridge, the railway was carried on brick arches above the street level, where the passenger departure platform with its two storey reception room was on the southern side, the Old Main Goods Warehouse standing on the northern side. Growth of traffic required the rapid expansion of the station and by 1849 there were as many as 64 wagon turntables. The passenger station was extended eastwards in 1837 by the addition of an arrival station, of which little is now known. Passenger services ceased on 4 May 1844, with the opening of a connecting line to Victoria Station.

HEW 100

SJ 830 979

The Old Main Goods Warehouse is the oldest surviving railway goods warehouse in the world. It is a simple structure deriving from a series of similar buildings used on inland waterways, although it does have character and size, being approximately 350 ft by 60 ft on a curve, with three storeys, two above rail and one at street level. It is of brick with stone casings to the doorways and it has ten gables. The floors, beams and columns are of wood.

HEW 955

SJ 829 979

The buildings at the former Liverpool Road Station have been conserved and redeveloped as part of the Museum of Science and Industry in Manchester.

Sources

BOOTH H. *An account of the Liverpool and Manchester Railway.* Wales & Baines, Liverpool, 1830.

TURNER R. Description of the iron roof over the railway station, Lime Street, Liverpool. *Min. Proc. Instn Civ. Engrs*, 1850, **9**, 204–214.

CARLSON R.E. *The Liverpool and Manchester Railway project.* David and Charles, Newton Abbot, 1969.

DONAGHY, T.J. *Liverpool and Manchester operations, 1831–1845.* David and Charles, Newton Abbot, 1972.

THOMAS R.H.G. *The Liverpool and Manchester Railway.* Batsford, London, 1980.

STOKER G. The oldest railway station in the world. *Railway Mag.*, 1902, **11**, 385–392.

16. Water Street Cast Iron Arch Bridge, Manchester

HEW 753

SJ 829 979

The need for a beam bridge having a flat soffit seems to have disappeared by the time the Manchester South Junction and Altrincham Railway was carried across Water Street.

Opened in 1848, this bridge has two railway tracks carried by six cast iron ribs, each cast in three sections, butted and bolted together. The span is about 50 ft and the bridge is on a slight skew.

The ribs are dumb-bell sections 6¾ in. wide by 2 ft 3 in. deep at the springing, reducing to 1 ft 10½ in. at the crown, with a rise of 7 ft. The spandrel bracing is of X-pattern, cruciform section, and there are panelled and decorated cast iron parapets. The sleepered track and ballast are carried on cast iron floorplates.

Other similar cast iron arch railway bridges exist nearby at Castlefield (SJ 828 975 to 841 974).

17. Grape Street Warehouse, Manchester

HEW 956

SJ 831 979

The Liverpool Road railway terminal has included many sheds and warehouses in its long history. Two were destroyed by fire in 1866 and the present Grape Street building was a replacement. It is a neat and compact structure of six storeys, four of them above rail level, showing eight windows and four hoist openings on its main elevation. Inside there are three rows of eight columns supporting 16 in. H-section beams lengthwise and 14 in. beams crosswise with wood floors. There is a twin hipped roof with queen post composite trusses.

It is an excellent example of its period and it forms, with Liverpool Road and Deansgate warehouses a unique set of three, namely the oldest, middle and newest railway warehouses, all visible from the same spot.

18. Deansgate Goods Warehouse, Manchester

The third, most recent, and largest of the three railway warehouses in the Liverpool Road area is a part of the former Great Northern Railway's Deansgate Goods Terminal and no longer in use as such.

HEW 957

SJ 835 978

It is a very large and relatively modern structure, opened in 1898. It was built by Robert Neill and Sons of Manchester with steelwork by Heenan and Froude of Newton Heath, Sir William Arrol of Glasgow and Keay and Sons of Darlaston; hydraulic handling equipment was supplied by Sir William Armstrong, Whitworth and Co. The resident engineer was W. T. Foxlee on behalf of successive chief engineers of the Great Northern Railway, namely Richard Johnson and Alexander Ross.

The building is 267 ft long by 217 ft wide by 75 ft high above street level, originally two goods sheds one above the other, with three warehouse floors above. It is built of red brick, banded with blue, and has fire-resistant floors on steel columns and beams. It had rail and road access on two levels and connection below via a feeder—the erstwhile Manchester and Salford Junction Canal—to the Manchester Ship Canal.

The Great Northern Railway acted as outlet to London and the south for the Manchester, Sheffield and Lincoln-shire Railway until the latter decided to build its own London extension and became the Great Central Rail-way. The Great Northern then decided to have its own major depot in Manchester with access from the tracks of the Cheshire Lines Committee.

Source

FOXLEE W.T. New goods station, Great Northern Railway, Manchester. *Engineer*, 1895, **86**, Sept., 221–225.

19. Victoria Station, Manchester

Within ten years of the opening of the Liverpool and Manchester Railway, developments elsewhere, notably the Manchester and Birmingham Railway and the pro-jected Manchester and Leeds Railway, determined the future of Liverpool Road Station. Alternative schemes

HEW 521

SJ 841 990

were considered and even favoured, but the opening of the Manchester and Bolton to Salford in 1838 and the Manchester and Leeds Railway to Oldham Road in 1839–41 led to an Act of 14 June 1839 for a new station at Hunts Bank, renamed Victoria, and another of 30 July 1842 for the Liverpool and Manchester Railway to link up with it. Trains were diverted at Miles Platting from Oldham Road to Hunts Bank on 1 January 1844 and the link was opened on 4 May 1844. There was one through common platform. Bolton trains were added from October 1846.

The west end eventually developed as part of the London and North Western Railway Exchange Station and the east end as the Lancashire and Yorkshire Railway Victoria Station. An even longer joint platform emerged in 1929 when platforms 3 and 11 became common to both stations, having an overall length of 2238 ft, the longest platform on Britain's railways, but shortened after closure of Exchange Station in 1980.

Victoria Station was extended southward towards Corporation Street in 1864. The plaques on the columns to the span between platforms 11 and 7 show 'W. Mabon, Ardwick Iron Works, Manchester'. The trusses of about 150 ft span have arched top booms and combined ties with ten bays of cross braced verticals, a less advanced form than in Liverpool Lime Street. Further extensions north and south in 1844 and 1904 gave Victoria a total of 17 platforms with further roofs. In 1995 a multi-purpose indoor entertainment and sports facility, Europe's largest, was opened here. The arena, built above the station, seats 19 500 spectators.

20. Piccadilly (London Road) Station, Manchester

HEW 451

SJ 848 978

This station was formerly jointly owned by the London, Midland and Scottish and the London and North Eastern Railways, arising from the 1842 Manchester and Birmingham line and the 1845 Manchester and Sheffield line via Woodhead.

Originally called Store Street, it became London Road in 1846 and Piccadilly in 1960. Major rebuilding of the roof took place in 1881 and there are now four spans of roof of 80 to 100 ft, supported on lattice girders on cast iron columns, two lines of single and one of twin.

The trusses, like those at Victoria and Liverpool Lime Street, have curved top booms and combined ties, the bracing being X-type at the centre and N-type elsewhere.

Sources

BIDDLE G. *Great railway stations of Britain.* David and Charles, Newton Abbot, 1986, 204–205.

BODY G. *Railway stations of Great Britain.* Patrick Stephens, Wellingborough, 1990.

21. Manchester Central Station

This building had by far the most impressive roof structure of all Manchester stations and, of all British Rail stations, was exceeded in span only by St Pancras.

Built in 1880 and similar in design to St Pancras, it has a span of 210 ft and a rise of 90 ft. The 16 ribs are curved Warren girders about 1 ft 3 in. deep. The contract drawings are signed by Andrew Handyside, contractors, of Derby, and Charles Sacré, A. Johnston and Richard Johnson, although the design was by Sir John Fowler.

HEW 450

SJ 837 977

Manchester
Central Station

Railway services ceased in 1969 and the building is now used as the GMEX exhibition centre.

Source

BIDDLE G. *Victorian stations*. David and Charles, Newton Abbot, 1973, 99–100, 140.

22. Dove Stone and Adjacent Reservoirs

Completion of Dove Stone Reservoir in 1966 brought to a conclusion the development, over a period of 90 years, of the water resources of Greenfield Brook and its Chew Brook tributary by the Ashton-under-Lyne, Stalybridge and Dukinsfield (District) Joint Waterworks Committee.

Yeoman Hey and Greenfield dams further upstream were completed in 1880 and 1902 respectively, their engineer being George Henry Hill. An interesting adjunct to these two reservoirs is the 1260 yard long tunnel through the mountain on their east side, emerging at the top of the high cascade just downstream of Yeoman Hey; it allowed the mill owners' entitlement to water to be conveyed before any was allowed into the reservoirs.

HEW 1650

SE 013 037

Chew Reservoir lies at the edge of a boggy plateau and at the head of a ravine, its overflow cill being exactly 1600 ft above Ordnance Datum. During the construction of the dam from 1907 to 1914, a major activity was the hauling of workmen, equipment and materials to this remote, elevated location. A 3 ft gauge tram-road was built from near Mossley to the jaws of the Chew Brook ravine, whereafter a cable-hauled incline rising 550 ft up the eastern face took over, followed by a further 'level' tram-road to the site. Much of the route of the lower tram-road is now occupied by a footpath.

A complex system of weirs, conduits and pipelines allowed water to be delivered into Yeoman Hey Reservoirs and to the pressure filter plant, which stood on the plateau at the head of Dove Stone Reservoir. A tunnel under the moorland also delivered water into Ashton's other reservoirs in the Swineshaw valley. The completion of Chew dam, the tunnel and the delivery mains was a considerable victory over hostile terrain and weather both for the engineers, G.H. Hill and Sons, and for the contractor, Morrison and Mason of Glasgow—the same team, in effect, which 20 years earlier had built Thirlmere Reservoir and parts of its delivery aqueduct. The tender amounted to £103 545 and the final payment to the contractor was £127 920.

Dove Stone dam, completed in 1966, is possibly the last large earth embankment dam to be built with a conventional puddle clay core, beneath which is a concrete-filled cut-off trench with an average depth of 75 ft. The engineers were again G.H. Hill and Sons, the landscape architect J.B. Blayney, and the contractor A.E. Farr & Co. The result of their efforts is an attractive dam set against the rugged scenery of the Peak District National Park and impounding 1100 million gallons of water. The embankment is 1840 ft long, 125 ft high, and contains 1 200 000 cubic yards of built-up material.

HEW 551

SE 014 036

The drop-shaft overflow at the north end, with a tunnel under the valley side, is a feature not usually seen at Pennine reservoirs and is in contrast with the impressive masonry cascade spillways of its earlier neighbours.

Source

LAWTON K.W. A historical perspective on the provision of a water supply to Saddleworth, a Pennine District. *Municipal Engineer*, 1994, 203–214.

23. Runcorn Railway Bridge

This important structure was built in 1868 to carry the London and North Western Railway across the River Mersey. Hitherto the route from London to Liverpool was via Warrington, Earlestown, and the Liverpool and Manchester Railway. The river is crossed by three main spans of 305 ft formed by wrought iron double-web lattice girders supported on stone piers. The overhead lattice bracing to the top flange is masked by stone portals which, perhaps unfortunately, are surmounted by castellated turrets in the Victorian Gothic revival style reaching to 50 ft above rail level. The bridge carries the railway 75 ft above the river to allow sufficient headroom for ships passing beneath. In order to achieve such a height in the approach to the bridge, the railway is carried on 59 brick arches on its rise to the Widnes end of the bridge.

HEW 196

SJ 509 835

RAILTRACK PLC

Runcorn Railway
Bridge

The engineer was William Baker, the contractor Thomas Brassey and the ironwork was supplied by J. Cochrane and Sons.

Source

The Runcorn Bridge, *Engineer*, June 1866, 472–473.

24. Runcorn–Widnes Road Bridge

HEW 1063

SJ 510 835

The 1082 ft main span of this elegant modern bridge, which crosses the River Mersey with a clearance of 75 ft, is longer than that of any other steel arch in Britain and is twice the span of the Tyne Bridge at Newcastle, the longest at the time of its opening in 1928.

Mott, Hay and Anderson designed the bridge to replace the former transporter bridge which was built in 1905, its 1000 ft span the longest and its 75 ft height the lowest of the five built in this country. A two-pinned bowstring arch design was adopted after wind tunnel model tests indicated that the presence of the adjacent railway bridge could, under certain wind conditions, produce severe oscillations if a conventional suspension

Runcorn–Widnes
Road Bridge

bridge design were to be used. Leonard Fairclough Ltd
and Dorman Long Ltd began construction in April 1956
and the bridge was opened in July 1961.

The bridge has side anchor spans of 250 ft, one crossing
the Manchester Ship Canal with a clearance of 80 ft. The
road was widened between 1975 and 1977 to four lanes,
with a single footpath cantilevered off the side of the road
deck.

Source

ANDERSON J.K. Runcorn–Widnes Bridge. *Proc. Instn Civ. Engrs*, 1964, **29,**
535–570.

25. Manchester Ship Canal

This 36 mile long ship canal is one of the most important
civil engineering projects of the late Victorian era. It took
six years to construct and was opened in 1894. It connects
the estuary of the River Mersey with docks built at Salford near the heart of the city of Manchester. There are
five sets of locks on the canal, the first being the entrance
locks at Eastham, and they give a total rise of 56 ft 6 in.

HEW 88

SJ 369 811 to
820 970

For most of its length the navigation channel is 120 ft wide and 28 ft deep. The canal cost over £15 million, and involved the excavation of 54 million cubic yards of earth and rock; at the peak of activity 17 000 people were employed on its construction. A wide variety of mechanical plant was also used, including 58 steam navvies, as well as cranes and railway locomotives and wagons.

The canal makes use of the River Irwell at the Manchester end and there are locks at Mode Wheel and Barton, to the west of the Bridgewater Canal Aqueduct. Near Irlam Locks the River Mersey is used, but from Thelwall on the M6 past Latchford Locks and south of Warrington the canal follows the left bank of the Mersey in a separate channel as far as Eastham.

The west coast main line railway, then the London and North Western Railway, was diverted westward on to a new high level bridge, designed by William Bean Farr, with severe gradients north and south. Parts of the old railway can still be seen on the up side. The two large bridges at Runcorn, already described, cross the canal as well as the river. The eastern terminus of the canal at

Manchester Ship Canal under construction

Salford Quays has been substantially redeveloped over recent years following the closure of Salford Docks.

The engineer was (Sir) Edward Leader Williams. The original contractor was Thomas A. Walker, but following his death in November 1889, the works were partially completed by direct labour under W. H. Topham, and the remainder by Sir John Jackson and C. J. Wills.

Source

The Manchester Ship Canal. *Engineering*, 1894, **57**, Jan., 97–142.

26. Bridgewater Canal

Following the opening of the Sankey Brook Canal in 1757, the third Duke of Bridgewater decided to build a canal from his mines at Worsley (SD 749 005) to carry coal to Manchester, and it was first authorized by an Act of 1759. Originally, it was proposed to lock down to the River Irwell at Barton, but the scheme was amended by an Act of 1760 to allow the canal to cross that river by a three-arch stone bridge, 39 ft above it, and to continue to Castlefield, Manchester, all on one level. This first section was opened on 17 July 1761, and it halved the cost of coal in Manchester. The engineers were James Brindley and John Gilbert.

From the terminal basin at Worsley a system of 46 miles of underground canals penetrated into the workings of the Duke's collieries under Walkden and Farnworth. These collieries, now worked out, still drain into the canal, causing discoloration for a mile each side of Worsley.

By 1772 the canal had been extended via Lymm to Runcorn (SJ 504 831) and later it was linked to the Trent and Mersey Canal—opened in 1777—at Preston Brook (SJ 567 810), to the Rochdale Canal at Castlefield (SJ 832 976) and to the Leeds and Liverpool Canal at Leigh (SJ 660 997), making it a vital link in the canal network of the North-West. Apart from the flight down to the river at Runcorn, it had only one lock.

The replacement of the Barton Aqueduct by a swing bridge in 1893 is dealt with in the next item. Of the old structure little remains, only the north abutment, a retaining wall and some arch stones re-erected alongside Bar-

HEW 976

SD 749 005 to 845 975

ton Lane. Later developments included the repeated raising of the canal in the Worsley area to maintain water
level, despite subsidence of the surrounding land.

Mining and commercial traffic ceased in 1974, but
pleasure cruising, including sightseeing trips from the
attractive packet-boat steps at Worsley, is booming. The
Worsley complex includes graving docks, which are still
in use.

27. Barton Aqueduct

HEW 28

SJ 767 976

At Barton the Manchester Ship Canal follows the line of
the River Irwell and as a result Brindley's fixed aqueduct
had to be replaced with a movable bridge.

The engineers, (Sir) Edward Leader Williams, James
Abernethy and William Henry Hunter, designed a swing
aqueduct which opens to permit the passage of vessels
on the ship canal and closes to allow traffic to pass along
the Bridgewater Canal. The swing span consists of an iron
trough 18 ft wide by 7 ft deep and 235 ft long, which holds

Barton Aqueduct

MANCHESTER SHIP CANAL CO. LTD

1500 tons of water. This is supported on cross girders carried by main steel N-type twin girders. The aqueduct swings about its centre line, which is on an island 400 ft by 30 ft. This also carries a road swing bridge. Before the aqueduct is moved, the ends of the trough are closed by gates sealed by rubber wedges. The total weight of the swinging structure is 1600 tons.

The contractors were C.J. Wills for the substructure, Andrew Handyside for the ironwork and Armstrong Mitchell and Co. for the machinery.

Source

WILLIAMS, SIR E.L. *et al.* The Manchester Ship Canal, *Min. Proc. Instn Civ. Engrs*, 1897, **131**, 14–99.

28. Transporter Bridge, Warrington

Joseph Crosfield built his first soapworks in 1814 at Bank Quay, Warrington, beside the River Mersey; a modern chemical factory still stands on the same site. In 1914 a transporter bridge was built to carry goods across the river to the works. It was designed by William Henry Hunter, built by Sir William Arrol, and opened in 1915. The bridge consists of a tower on either bank which is carried by mass concrete cellular foundations. Double cantilevers on each tower support a suspended central span and the whole structure is built out of riveted mild steel plates and angles, with extensive use being made of laced and battened members. The car was originally designed to carry rail traffic of up to 18 tons in weight, and it was modified in 1940 to take road traffic as well. Further modifications in 1950 increased its capacity to 30 tons, and increased its length to its present 339 ft overall. The structure is 30 ft wide, and has a clearance of 76 ft at high water level. It has a clear span of 200 ft between the towers.

HEW 140

SJ 597 877

The two other remaining transporter bridges in this country are at Middlesbrough and at Newport, Gwent.

Source

FORBES N.N. *Transporter Bridges*. Light Railway Transport League, no date, 10.

29. Lower Gorton Reservoir

HEW 2013

SJ 894 960

The Stockport branch of the Ashton Canal (circa 1800) was carried over the valley of Gore Brook on an embankment 30 ft high. In 1823–25 the Manchester and Salford Waterworks Company created a reservoir by lining the upstream face of the embankment with puddle clay and building up a combined outlet shaft at the upstream end of the culvert, thus creating what may have been one of the first impounding reservoirs for communal water supply and the only dam with a canal, filled in during the 1960s, along its crest. The engineer appears to have been Nicholas Brown, who was involved in canal construction. In 1842–43 James Simpson prescribed and added a new, more adequate, overflow shaft and tunnel and a better draw-off tower.

In 1876–79 Manchester Waterworks, under the direction of John Frederic Bateman, constructed a large brick-built culvert to divert the polluted brook around the east side of this and the upstream reservoir and so utilize them for the storage of imported water. The reservoir was last used for water supply in 1950 and now forms part of the adjoining public park.

30. Stockport Viaduct

HEW 569

SJ 891 903

Immortalized by L.S. Lowry, but tending to be hidden by modern building developments, this viaduct is 1792 ft long and 110 ft high where it crosses the River Mersey in the centre of Stockport. It was completed in 1842 for the Manchester and Birmingham Railway. The designer was George Watson Buck, a former resident engineer for the construction of the London and Birmingham Railway, and the author of a treatise on oblique bridges. The contractors were John Tomkinson, and Samuel and John Holme. The viaduct has 26 arches, 22 of them of equal 63 ft span, and is constructed mainly of brick with stone features at the base of the piers; the cost was £72 000. The same dimensions and form of construction were retained when the viaduct was widened in 1890 to accommodate four tracks. Centring and scaffolding used during the

original construction were re-used for Dane Viaduct, some 15 miles to the south and on the same line.

Stockport Viaduct

Source

BROWN W.E.S. Railways in 1841. *Railway Mag.*, 1922, **50**, Apr., 253.

31. Brabyns Park Bridge, Marple

The River Goyt is crossed by the neat and attractive cast iron arch bridge in Brabyns Park, made in 1813 by Salford Iron Works. The three ribs span 50 ft in two segments. The spandrels carry the diminishing ring pattern, the rise is about 1 in 11 and the width 12 ft. There is a post and three-rail parapet fence with central motif carrying the letter W above the date. The masonry abutments and pilasters are of distinctive design.

HEW 828

SJ 963 902

32. Marple Aqueduct

Benjamin Outram built this aqueduct in 1800 to carry the Peak Forest Canal over the River Goyt. The canal connected Whaley Bridge with the Ashton Canal at Dukinfield, 15 miles to the north. The aqueduct is situated at the foot of a flight of 16 locks which are themselves crossed

HEW 26

SJ 955 900

BRITISH WATERWAYS BOARD

Marple Aqueduct   by two small bridges. It has three 60 ft semicircular arches of solid masonry with pierced spandrels and is about 90 ft high. The lower halves of the piers are in rough stone with rounded ends. The upper piers have narrow and graceful pilasters, each with a curved batter. There is a good view of this famous aqueduct from the adjacent railway viaduct. The canal is now disused except for pleasure purposes.

Source

SCHOFIELD, R.B. Benjamin Outram (1764–1805), canal engineer extraordinary. *Proc. Instn Civ. Engrs*, 1979, **66**, 543–545.

Additional sites

Numbers in bold type indicate Historical Engineering Works (HEW) site numbers.

1. Northumberland

Haltwhistle Bridge, **1043**, NY 705 637

Hexham Station Roof, **924**, NY 941 644

Morwick Water Tower, **516**, NU 239 036

Whittle Dene Valve House, **1952**, NZ 076 673

Wydon Burn Reservoir, Hexham, **2055**, NY 932 632

2. Tyne and Wear

Cast Iron Arch Bridge, North Shields, **35**, NZ 359 688

Chimney Windmill, Newcastle, **988**, NZ 240 655

Glass-making Cone (brick tower), Lemington, **142**, NZ 184 646

Manor Chare Bridge, Newcastle, **730**, NZ 253 641

Newburn Bridge, **991**, NZ 165 652

No. 8 Dry Dock, North Shields, **1994**, NZ 355 673

Robert Stephenson's Works, Forth Street, Newcastle, **990**, NZ 247 637

Salters Bridge, Newcastle, **1327**, NZ 255 685

Swalwell Pipe Bridge, **1953**, NZ 198 624

Victoria Tunnel, Newcastle, **179**, NZ 236 654 to 264 641

3. County Durham and Cleveland

Lamb Bridge, Lambton Castle, **1044**, NZ 294 524

Newton Cap Viaduct, Bishop Auckland, **992**, NZ 206 303

Saltburn Station Roof, **989**, NZ 664 215

4. Cumbria

Eamont Bridge, **986**, NY 522 288

Lanercost Ancient Road Bridge, **306**, NY 553 633

Ulverston Canal, **619**, SD 293 785 to 314 777

5. York and North Yorkshire

Bootham Bar, York, **555**, SE 601 522

Fountains Abbey Guest House Bridge, **1334**, SE 273 682

Fountains Abbey West Bridge, **1335**, SE 272 682

Kexby Ancient Road Bridge, **678**, SE 705 511

Pocklington Station Roof, **912**, SE 802 487

Roman Sewer, York, **218**, SE 604 517

Scarborough Branch Railway Bridge, York, **195**, SE 596 521

Skelton Railway Bridge, near York, **326**, SE 565 553

Suspension Bridge, Huttons Ambo, **789**, SE 765 677

York Minster, Chapter House Roof, **748**, SE 603 522

York Minster, Strengthening of Central Tower, **14**, SE 603 522

6. South and West Yorkshire

Abbeydale Industrial Hamlet, Sheffield, **951**, SK 325 820

Abbot's Staith Warehouse, Selby, **782**, SE 616 326

Astley Cast Iron Bridge, **343**, SE 396 282

Cawood Swing Bridge, **786**, SE 574 378

Drax Power Station Chimney, **11**, SE 665 268

Elsecar Colliery Pumping Engine, **220**, SE 388 000

Emley Moor TV Mast, **15**, SE 222 130

Fairburn Cast Iron Arch Bridge, **346**, SE 479 275

Huddersfield, Locomotive Bridge, **1307**, SE 150 168

Kirkstall Viaduct, Leeds, **291**, SE 279 342

Naburn Locks, River Ouse, **1178**, SE 596 445

Roman Road, Blackstone Edge, **916**, SD 966 169

Roman Road, Wheeldale, Goathland, **824**, SE 810 985

Sheffield Canal Aqueduct, **1**, SK 383 887

Slaithwaite Dam, **757**, SE 075 141

Walton Hall Cast Iron Bridge, Wakefield, **438**, SE 363 163

Wortley Top Forge, Sheffield, **1157**, SE 294 998

7. Lancashire and Isle of Man

Castle Mill, Quernmore, Lancaster, **1289**, SD 520 609

Clapper Bridges, Wycoller, **1401**, SD 932 392

Dunsop 'New' Bridge, River Hodder, **1624**, SD 663 494

Hamer Pasture Dam, **544**, SD 896 162

Lower Hodder Bridge, **1403**, SD 704 393

Marton Mere Drainage, Blackpool, **1350**, SD 34 35

Morecambe Central Pier, **1290**, SD 436 646

Paythorne Bridge, River Ribble, **1790**, SD 831 513

Penwortham Old Bridge, Preston, **1348**, SD 529 283

Preesall Salt Mines, Lancashire, **1351**, SD 33 44

Preston Docks, **1127**, SD 515 295

Preston Station Roof, **984**, SD 534 290

Ribchester Bridge, River Ribble, **1789**, SD 662 356

St Anne's Pier, **1007**, SD 318 286

Whalley Bridge, River Ribble, **1791**, SD 732 359

8. Merseyside and Greater Manchester

Bradshaw Brook Viaduct, Bolton, **250**, SD 727 171

Chapel Milton Viaducts, **1799**, SK 055 818 and 056 818

Crosshall Reservoir, Wirral, **1254**, SJ 279 843

Everton Water Tower, **1253**, SJ 361 918

Greater Manchester Metrolink, **1891**, SD 804 105 to SJ 770 879

Kearsley Bridge, **1266**, SD 753 053

Liverpool Overhead Railway, **1938**, SJ 336 968 to 362 876

Middleton (Scowcroft) Cast Iron Bridge, **929**, SD 887 065

Newton-le-Willows Viaduct, **932**, SJ 593 953

Newton-le-Willows Water Tower, **731**, SJ 599 956

Stalybridge Aqueduct, **858**, SJ 954 982

Stockport Market Hall, **1673**, SJ 897 904

Store Street Aqueduct, Manchester, **1792**, SJ 850 981

Warrington; A49 Reinforced Concrete Arch, **254**, SJ 608 879

General bibliography

Adamson S. H. *Seaside piers.* Batsford, London, 1977.

Baldwin C.E. *The historical development of the Port of Blyth.* Newcastle upon Tyne, 1929.

Baughan R.E. *The Midland Railway north of Leeds.* David and Charles, Newton Abbot, 1987.

Beaver P. *A history of lighthouses.* Peter Davies, London, 1971.

Biddle G. *Victorian stations.* David and Charles, Newton Abbot, 1973.

Biddle G. *Great railway stations of Britain.* David and Charles, Newton Abbot, 1986.

Biddle G. *The railway surveyors.* Ian Allan, London, 1990.

Biddle G. and Nock O.S. *The railway heritage of Britain.* Michael Joseph, London, 1983.

Binnie G.M. *Early Victorian water engineers.* Thomas Telford, London, 1981.

Binnie G.M. *Early dam builders in Britain.* Thomas Telford, London, 1987.

Blower A. *British railway tunnels.* Ian Allan, London, 1964.

Body G. *Railway stations of Britain.* Patrick Stephens, Wellingborough, 1990.

Brees S.C. *Railway practice.* John Williams, London, 2nd Series, 1840.

British bridges. Public Works, Roads and Transport Congress, London, 1933.

Chrimes M.M. *Civil engineering, 1839–1889: a photographic history.* Thomas Telford, London, 1991.

Coleman T. *The railway navvies.* Hutchinson, London, 1965.

Cossons N. *The BP book of industrial archaeology.* David and Charles, Newton Abbot, 1975.

Cresy E. *Encyclopaedia of civil engineering.* Longman, London, 1856.

Dow G. *Great Central.* Locomotive Publishing, London, 1959–65.

Fairbairn W. *The application of cast iron and wrought iron to building purposes.* Weale, London, 1857.

Hadfield C. *The canals of Yorkshire and North East England.* David and Charles, Newton Abbot, 1972.

Hadfield C. and Biddle G. *The canals of North West England.* David and Charles, Newton Abbot, 1970.

Hadfield C. and Skempton A.W. *William Jessop, engineer.* David and Charles, Newton Abbot, 1979.

Hague D.B. and Christie R. *Lighthouses: their architecture, history and archaeology.* Gomer Press, Llandysul, 1975.

Hoole K. *A regional history of the railways of England,: 4. North Eastern England.* David and Charles, Newton Abbot, 1965.

Humber W. *Cast iron and wrought iron bridges and girders for railway structures.* Spon, London, 1857.

Irvine R.J. *The North Eastern Railway Company, 1870–1914.* Leicester University Press, 1976.

Jervoise E. *The ancient bridges of the North of England.* Architectural Press, London, 1931.

Johnson R.W. *The making of the river Tyne.* Walter Scott, Newcastle upon Tyne, 1895.

Labrum E.A. (ed.) *Civil engineering heritage: Eastern and Central England.* Thomas Telford, London, 1994.

Leech Sir B. *History of the Manchester Ship Canal.* Sherratt and Hughes, Manchester and London, 1907.

Marshall C.F.D. *A centenary history of the Liverpool and Manchester Railway.* Locomotive Publishing, London, 1930.

Marshall J. *The Lancashire and Yorkshire Railway*. David and Charles, Newton Abbot, 1969.

Otter R.A. (ed.) *Civil engineering heritage: Southern England*. Thomas Telford, London, 1994.

Penfold A. (ed.) *Thomas Telford, engineer.* Thomas Telford, London, 1980.

Priestley J. *Navigable rivers, canals, and railways throughout Great Britain*. Longman, London, 1831.

Reed B. *Crewe to Carlisle*. Ian Allan, London, 1969.

Richards J.M. *National Trust book of bridges*. Jonathan Cape, London, 1984.

Rolt L.T.C. *George and Robert Stephenson*. Longman, London, 1960.

Ruddock E.C. *Arch bridges and their builders, 1735–1835*. Cambridge University Press, 1979.

Sandstrom G.E. *The history of tunnelling*. Barrie and Rockliff, London, 1963.

Simmons J. *The Victorian railway*. Thames and Hudson, New York, 1991.

Sivewright W.J. (ed.) *Civil engineering heritage: Wales and Western England*. Thomas Telford, London, 1986.

Skempton A.W. (ed.) *John Smeaton, FRS*. Thomas Telford, London, 1981.

Smith N. *A history of dams*. Peter Davies, London, 1971.

Steel W.L. *The history of the London and North Western Railway*. Railway and Travel Monthly, London, 1914.

Tomlinson W.W. *The North Eastern Railway*. Longmans Green, London, 1914.

Walmisley A.T. *Iron roofs*. Spon, London, 1888.

Whishaw F. *The railways of Great Britain and Ireland*. Simpkin Marshall, London, 1840.

Wryde J.S. *British lighthouses*. Unwin, London, 1913.

Name index

Engineers

Architects

Contractors

Subject index

Numbers in **bold type** indicate Historical Engineering Works (HEW) site numbers.